VOLUME 10

FUNK & WAGNALLS WILDLIFE ENCYCLOPEDIA

GENERAL EDITORS • Dr. Maurice Burton and Robert Burton

Also published as The International Wildlife Encyclopedia and
Encyclopedia of Animal Life.

Funk & Wagnalls, Inc., New York, New York

Hydra

The hydra's simple tubular body with its crown of tentacles has earned it a place in every elementary textbook of zoology and made it the object of many detailed studies. It is one of the few freshwater coelenterates, the bulk of which are marine. The body of a hydra is a bag whose wall is made up of two layers of cells separated only by a very thin layer of non-cellular material. The tentacles, which usually number 5 or 6 but may be as few as 4 or as many as 12, are hollow. They surround the mouth, while the other end of the body is a basal disc which normally anchors the hydra by a sticky secretion. Though often abundant in ponds, hydras frequently escape notice

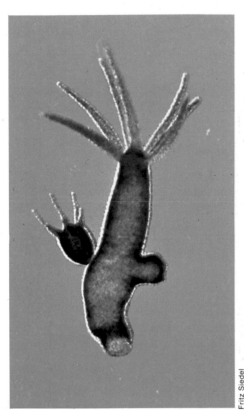

△ *Chips off the old block: a parent hydra with two buds, one advanced, one very very young.*

because of their habit of retracting into a tiny blob when disturbed.

Both tentacles and body are very extensible, for the bases of many of the cells are drawn out as muscle fibres — those of the outer layer of cells running lengthwise and those of the inner layer running around the body. The nervous system co-ordinating the movements is extremely simple, consisting of only a network of nerve cells. There is no brain of any sort.

There are three species of hydra in Britain. The green hydra **Chlorohydra viridissima**, which used to be called **Hydra viridis**, has short tentacles that are never as long as the body. The

brown hydra, **Hydra (Pelmatohydra) oligactis**, has tentacles 4—5 times the length of the body, which is usually clearly divided into a stomach region and a narrower stalk. These two species are found throughout the world and their colours are caused by single-celled algae living within their cells. When animal prey is scarce the hydra draws nourishment from these algae. In both species the body may be as much as 1¼ in. long but it is usually much shorter. The third species found in Britain is the slender hydra **Hydra attenuata**. Its body is never much more than ½ in. in length when fully extended, it lacks a stalk, and its tentacles are never more than 3 times the length of the body.

The stinging cells

Hydras, like their relatives the sea anemones and jellyfishes, have stinging cells with which they capture their prey. Each stinging cell or nematocyst is a rounded cell with a hollow coiled thread inside that can be shot out at great speed (see anemone p 44).

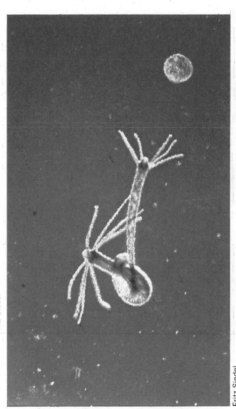

△ *Budded hydra almost ready to break free while a* **Volvox**-*like 'plant animal' just escapes.*

Hydra has four kinds. In one kind the thread is shot into the prey, injecting a poison. In a second kind the thread coils after it is shot out, and if the prey has bristles of any kind these tend to become entangled in it. The third type of nematocyst is probably truly defensive. It is shot out at animals not normally eaten by the hydra. The fourth kind of nematocyst is used to fasten the tentacles when the hydra is walking. This is not strictly a stinging cell although it looks very like it, and is best referred to as a thread capsule. In fact, some people prefer to use

the term 'thread capsule' for all of them, simply because some of them do not sting.

When a nematocyst is discharged, its thread is forced inside out like a stocking, except that forces inside the thread itself are responsible for driving it out. The nematocysts used in capturing prey are discharged when the prey touches a little trigger on the side of the cell. Touch, however, is not enough, for the stinging cell must also be stimulated by chemicals in the water that are given out by the prey.

In all types, the stinging cells cannot be used again but are replaced by new ones migrating in from other parts of the body.

Progressing by somersaults

Although normally anchored, hydra can move about by creeping slowly on its basal disc in a sort of sliding movement. It can move more rapidly by a looping movement or a series of somersaults. To do this, a

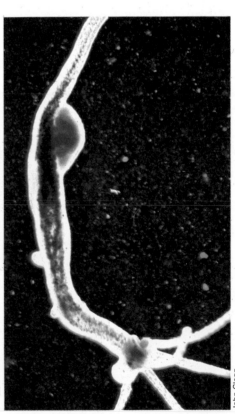

△ *Hydra forming an ovary for sexual reproduction. It does this in harsh conditions.*

hydra bends over and gets a grip with special thread capsules on the tentacles. It lets go with its basal disc and brings this over in turn, very much like somebody doing 'cartwheels'. Hydras can also float at the surface of the water buoyed up by gas bubbles given out by the basal disc. The characteristic feature of the behaviour of hydras is that they suddenly contract into a tight ball every 5 or 10 minutes, for no obvious reason. This happens less often at night than by day.

Snagging its prey

The diet includes insect larvae, water fleas, worms, even newly-hatched fishes and tadpoles. Between meals the tentacles are held outstretched and more or less still, but at the approach of prey they start to writhe and later they bend in towards the open mouth. They will do these things if offered only extracts from other animals without any solids. For example, the juice from crushed water fleas alone will make a hydra go through the motions of putting food into its mouth. In fact a single chemical—glutathione—is responsible. If, however, the prey touches the tentacle the threads of the nematocysts are shot out, it is caught, held and paralysed, then carried to the mouth and swallowed. The mouth can open wide enough to take in animals that are themselves wider than the body of the hydra, which will stretch to accommodate them. Once inside the baglike body of the hydra, the prey is partially digested by enzymes given out by the inner layer of cells. Small particles breaking off are engulfed by individual cells for the final stages of digestion and indigestible particles are rejected through the mouth.

While food is in the body whiplike flagella on the cells of the inner layer are stirring the food around the inside of the body, a churning which aids digestion.

Multiplying in two ways

Hydra reproduce both sexually and by budding. Most species of hydra reproduce sexually in autumn or early winter although some do so in spring or early summer. One thing that can cause sexual reproduction, even out of season, is an accumulation of carbon dioxide in the water—as happens when a number of hydras are overcrowded. There are no special reproductive organs but small cells appear as bulges on the body in the upper half. Ovaries which are borne on different individuals in most species appear lower down on the body, also as bulges, each containing a single large egg-cell, or ovum. The ripe ovum pushes through the outer layer of the hydra's body and the cells around it form a little cup or cushion for the ovum. The male cells or sperms are shed into the water where they swim about and eventually reach the ova and fertilise them. The embryo which results from the division of the fertilised ovum secretes around itself a hard, sticky yellow shell $\frac{1}{50}$ to $\frac{1}{25}$ in. across. The shell may be smooth on the outside or spiny, according to the species. Thus enclosed, the embryo can survive drying and freezing. After lying dormant for 3—10 weeks it breaks out of its capsule, grows tentacles and becomes a new hydra, a perfect miniature of the adult.

Budding technique

New hydras can also be formed by buds. Each bud begins as a little bump on the side of the body. This grows out, and an opening

E Grave

△ *Murder in miniature: after paralysing a water flea with stinging cells and drawing it in with sticky threads and tentacles, a hydra stretches its mouth round an outsize victim.*

▽ *Coelenterate mealtime: the green hydra at left is stinging a water flea into submission, the one at right is swollen with similar repast (9 × life size).*

Heather Angel

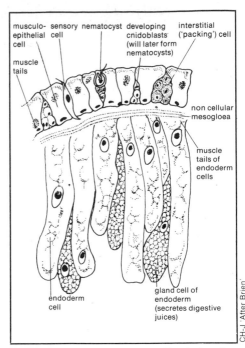

musculo-epithelial cell
sensory cell
nematocyst
developing cnidoblasts (will later form nematocysts)
interstitial ('packing') cell
muscle tails
non cellular mesogloea
muscle tails of endoderm cells
endoderm cell
gland cell of endoderm (secretes digestive juices)

CH-J 'After Brien'

△ *Cross-section through body wall of hydra. It has only two layers of cells. The inner (endoderm) cells are for food breakdown. The outer (ectoderm) cells perform all other functions.*

appears at its free end. Tentacles are pushed out all round the mouth and finally the bud breaks away from the parent, settles down and grows into a new hydra, the whole process occupying 2 days, and a single hydra may bear several buds at once.

Inside-out hydras

In Greek mythology Hercules found himself trying to kill a monster called Hydra which had many heads. As fast as Hercules cut off one head another grew in its place. In 1744, Abraham Trembley, Swiss tutor to the children of the Comte de Bentinck, published his story of another hydra—the animal we are concerned with here. Trembley had found that a complete hydra would be regenerated from only ⅛th of the parent body. He also succeeded in turning these animals inside out, a remarkably delicate operation which he performed by threading them on horse hairs. Trembley showed that the hydras would survive even this drastic operation. These experiments caught on and for a while became very popular among certain scientists. More recently, they have been pursued in much greater detail. We now know that even tinier pieces of hydra, even a piece only $\frac{6}{1000}$ in. long, will grow into a new hydra provided that cells

from both layers of the wall of the parent body are present. Even if the cells are separated into a mush of independent cells, these will come together to form a new hydra. The experiments are called 'Dissociation and Regeneration'.

We also know now that when a hydra is turned inside out it gets back to normal because the cells of the two layers migrate past each other to get into their proper positions. In fact, hydras are continually remodelling themselves and replacing old cells with new. If the tissues just below the tentacles of a hydra are marked with dye, they can be seen to move gradually down to the basal disc, eventually being lost and replaced by growth of new cells in the region from which they started.

phylum	**Coelenterata**
class	**Hydrozoa**
order	**Hydrida**
family	**Hydridae**
genera & species	***Chlorohydra viridissima*** *green hydra* ***Hydra attenuata*** *slender hydra* ***H. oligactis*** *brown hydra others*

▽ *Stuck to a water plant by special cells in their basal discs, five brown hydras hang in wait for the touch or taste of prey (7 × life size).*

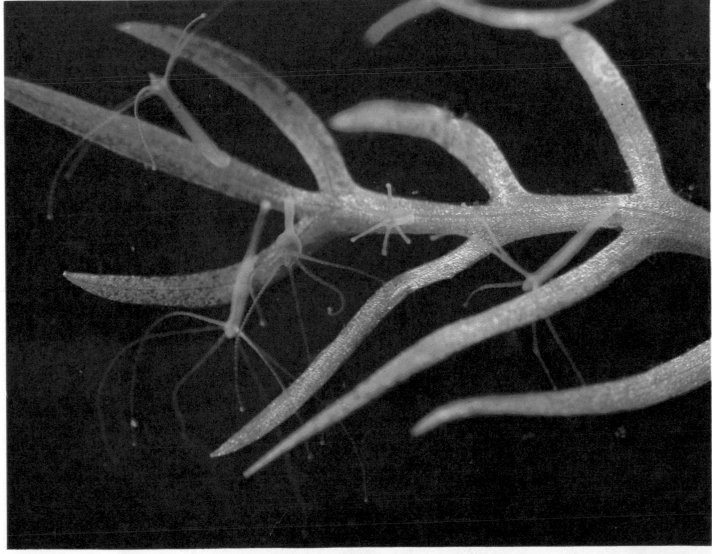

Heather Angel

Hyrax

The hyrax has been described as a zoological puzzle, a natural hotchpotch and a museum of antiquities. Although only rabbit-sized, it is usually called the nearest relative of the elephant!

The dozen species of rock hyraxes and tree hyraxes make up a single family in the order Hyracoidea. Small, thick-set, greyish-brown and rabbit-like, tail-less with short muzzles and small round ears, the largest are no more than 18 in. long. The forefeet have four functional toes, the fifth being a mere stump. The hindfeet have three toes, the inner toe having a curved claw. All the other toes have short hoof-like nails. The best known are the Cape hyrax or dassie of Cape Province and Southwest Africa and the daman or cherogil—the conies of the Bible—of Syria to Sinai and southern Arabia. There are many species and subspecies: in the Transvaal, Angola, East Africa, Ethiopia and the Sudan, in the Congo, Nigeria and the Cameroons. Tree hyraxes live in South and East Africa, in the equatorial forests, in Fernando Po and Zanzibar.

Their skeleton has much in common with that of the rhinoceros, but is remarkable for the large number of ribs. The teeth are most unusual, and since teeth are much used in classifying mammals this makes things difficult. The single pair of upper cutting teeth (incisors) are rodent-like except that instead of being flat with chisel edges they are prismatic and end in sharp points. The lower front teeth include two pairs of rooted teeth unlike those of rodents; the outer pair are nearly horizontal and their crowns are divided into three lobes. There is a gap between the front teeth and the cheek teeth like the gap, known as the diastema, in rodents. The upper cheek teeth are like those of a rhinoceros, the lower cheek teeth like those of a hippopotamus.

Noisy family groups

Rock hyraxes are usually timid and in-offensive as well as shy but they can be aggressive at times. Their safety lies in being able to seek shelter quickly. It is said that, when feeding, they have a look-out who gives warning of danger by shrill shrieks. They are noisy and this alone probably gives them protection, for danger or 'all clear' signals can be heard over a wide area. Tree hyraxes seek safety in holes in trees but whereas most tree-climbers have a tail for use as a balancer hyraxes have none. They have no sharp claws nor grasping fingers but they have rubbery pads on their feet. Rock hyraxes use these to scamper over smooth faces of rock and tree hyraxes to run up smooth trunks.

Colonies of hyraxes may contain 6—50 individuals; the larger colonies are made up of family groups of females and young and one old male. When alarmed they scamper for a hole in the rocks or in the ground, the old male bringing up the rear. Although all hyraxes are active mainly by day they are on the alert on moonlit nights, when their calls may be heard. The call is a mewing note which may rise higher and higher to end in a prolonged scream. This may be answered by another hyrax as far as a mile away. The alarm note, as when a bird of prey flies overhead, is a short, coarse bark. The daily pattern is for all members of the colony to come out at dawn to sun them-

◁△ *That belligerent look: a hyrax glowers suspiciously from its retreat in the rocks.*
◁ *Barrel of fur: a thirsty rock hyrax.*

selves on a rock, all clumped together. As the sun warms up they slowly spread out, grooming and stretching. Then they feed for about an hour, the tree hyrax climbing trees, especially acacia, to feed on leaves, rock hyraxes feeding mainly on grass but also on herbs and low bushes. An hour before noon they move into shade to rest and come out again about 5 hours later to feed for a further 2 hours.

Slow breeding, many enemies

There are usually 2–3 in a litter after a gestation of 225 days. The babies are born fully furred and with eyes open. They begin nibbling food at 2 days. They become sexually mature after 2 years and the maximum life span in captivity is nearly 6 years. Slow breeders, they nevertheless keep up their numbers in spite of many enemies. Snakes such as cobra and puff adder, large eagles, Mackinder's owl and the augur buzzard are their main enemies, but hyraxes are also killed by leopard, hunting dog and caracal, and the smaller beasts of prey such as mongooses.

Scientists' joy

When the Bible was translated into English, coney—meaning a rabbit—was the nearest the translators could get to naming this strange mammal. The name 'hyrax' is Greek for shrew, but the first scientific account of the animal was not given until 1766, when it was called *Cavia capensis*, a kind of guinea pig. The first Dutch settlers in South Africa called it *dasje* or little badger, now spelt dassie. It was then called a rodent but Cuvier, the French anatomist, decided it must be related to the hoofed animals. It has, as we have seen, some teeth like the rhinoceros and others like the teeth of a hippopotamus. The bones of its forelegs and feet are like those of elephants; its brain is unlike that of a rodent and more like the brain of an elephant and its stomach is nearer that of a horse. Its hindfeet with the

△△ *Alert tree hyrax* **Dendrohyrax arboreus.**
▷ *Grazing rock hyraxes. The white back fur covers glands.* ▽ *Hyrax at ease in the sun.*

three toes and hoof-like nails recall the hindfeet of the horse's ancestor. The placenta by which the unborn hyrax is attached in the womb is halfway between that of an elephant and that of a horse. And to complete this mixture of rodent and hoofed animal characters, the tree hyrax has a gland in the middle of its back surrounded by white hairs which are erected in moments of excitement. A gland like this is found on the top of the head of the capybara, the huge South American rodent, which also has hindlegs with three toes like the ancestor of the horse, and like the tapir.

The fossil record suggests that horses, tapirs, rhinoceroses, hippopotamuses and elephants had a common ancestor a long way back in time. Although they all look so different today their differences tend to disappear as we trace back along their family tree. The further we go back in time the more their ancestors had in common—and if there is one animal alive today that more than any other shows relationships with the ancestors of all these large hoofed animals it is the hyrax. It may sound absurd to call this animal, the size of a large guinea pig, the paterfamilias of these huge pachyderms but there is a strong degree of truth in it.

Philippa Scott

class	**Mammalia**
order	**Hyracoidea**
family	**Procaviidae**
genera & species	***Dendrohyrax dorsalis*** *tree hyrax* ***Procavia capensis*** *rock hyrax others*

KB Newman

Donald Paterson: WWF

Ibex

The name 'ibex' is applied to seven high-mountain forms of wild goat. By common consent the markhor is excluded, being somewhat different from the rest. Even so ibexes are a varied lot. It is still not certain whether they are all closely interrelated, or whether some of them may not have been derived independently from the true wild goat or bezoar, which inhabits low-lying but hilly desert country. Most ibexes are larger and more thickset than the bezoar and their horns are broad and rounded in front with evenly spaced knots on this surface, instead of the narrow, keeled front surface of the bezoar. The horns of most ibexes are scimitar-shaped, as in the bezoar, but the Spanish and the two East Caucasus species—locally known as **tur***—have very divergent horns which turn up, out, back and down, and finally in and up.*

The Siberian ibex, especially those from the Tienshan mountains, have the longest horns. The Caucasian turs have very thick horns compared with their length, while in the bezoar and the Nubian ibex the horns are very slender. In the Siberian ibex and the walia the knots on the front surface of the horns are bold and well-developed; in the Nubian, Alpine and West Caucasus (Kuban) species, however, the outer edge of the front surface is somewhat bevelled-off, and the knots are clear only toward the inner edge. The Daghestan tur has no knots on the horns, while in the Spanish ibex the horns are actually keeled on their front surface like the bezoar. Females in all these species are very similar, with short, backturned horns.

Some species are brownish with black stripes down the outside of the limbs, along the lower flanks, along the middle of the back, and down the nose, while the belly is white. The bezoar also has a black stripe on the shoulders. These markings are sometimes almost or entirely lost. They are always less developed in the females, while in the Siberian ibex they are very faint in winter coat. In some Siberian ibex from the Tienshan and Kashmir there is a large white 'saddle' mark in winter.

Adult males of Siberian ibex weigh 180–220 lb; occasionally, as in the large Tienshan and Pamir race, as much as 290 lb; while females weigh only 70–90, occasionally up to 130 lb.

Up and down the mountains

Thanks to the work of Russian zoologists as well as sportsmen, the habits of the Siberian ibex are fairly well known. It lives between 1 700 and 17 000 ft above sea level, even higher in the Pamir, in steeper country than the wild sheep living in the same mountains. Herds consist of 3–40, in places up to 200, especially during the coldest months. In winter, the ibex move to steeper slopes with less snow, often south-facing. This may involve a downward migration of 1 000–6 500 ft, which sometimes brings the ibex into the forest zone, where some stay the whole year. At night ibex may move down the mountainside to avoid frosts and move up again to feed at 10 or 11 am. They eat mainly grass and herbs in the summer and mainly leaves in winter.

△ *An ibex challenges its companions, sure of its ability to master the most precarious of ledges.*

◁ *Room with a view: alpine ibex at rest.*

A Molinier: Jacana

Enforced celibacy

The rut takes place in autumn, or as late as December or early January in some parts of central Asia. It lasts 7–10 days, the males feeding little at this time. They fight among themselves to form harems, rearing on their hindlegs and clashing their horn-bases together, like wild sheep. This specialised method of fighting causes no injury but ensures that the largest males with the thickest horns win. So a male has not much chance of gathering a harem until about 6 years old, although he may become sexually mature at 1½ years. The old males gather huge harems in which each year 15–20% of the females stay barren. Gestation lasts 170–180 days, and the single young weighing 8–9 lb is born around May. About 5% of females have twins. They are not weaned until autumn, but begin to graze after a month or so. Siberian ibex are thought to live 15–20 years. In the Nubian ibex, the rut occurs in September and October, gestation is shorter, 150–160 days, so the young are born from February to April. In the bezoar, the young are born in May, in dense bush or forest; the young of true ibex hide by day in the rocks.

Fighting with their horns

Young ibex are preyed upon by eagles, jackals and foxes; adults by leopards, snow leopards, bears, lynxes and wolves. They normally seek safety in flight, but can fight with their horns when cornered.

How many species?

There is a division of opinion on whether there are seven species of ibex or fewer than this. Some writers claim there are only five. One sure way to tell if two kinds of animals represent different species is if they remain distinct in the wild state, without forming a hybrid population between them. If there is a hybrid population there will be many intermediates between two 'pure' forms, which will then cease to be separated. Most of the ibex species live in different places and have no chance to interbreed. There is, therefore, no definite way to tell whether they are real species or not. Bringing members of different species together in captivity to see if they will interbreed does not give us an answer because under the unnatural conditions of a zoo paddock things can happen that would not occur in the wild. For example, lions and tigers interbreed in zoos

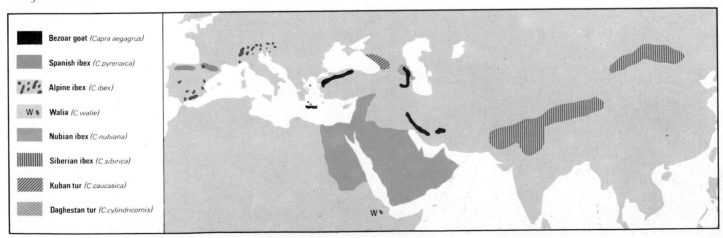

Bezoar goat (*Capra aegagrus*)

Spanish ibex (*C. pyrenaica*)

Alpine ibex (*C. ibex*)

W Walia (*C. walie*)

Nubian ibex (*C. nubiana*)

Siberian ibex (*C. sibirica*)

Kuban tur (*C. caucasica*)

Daghestan tur (*C. cylindricornis*)

and although they used to live more or less side by side in the same habitat in India, Iran and Iraq, they did not interbreed.

During the last Ice Age Spanish and alpine ibex co-existed in southern France and apparently did not hybridize. Our evidence for this is that all specimens as well as all cave paintings of these animals show either one or the other, never a mixture. In the central Caucasus today two species of tur live side by side in an area 21 by 24 miles, this area representing 15% of the total range of the Kuban tur and 10% of the range of the Daghestan tur. In that part of the overlap which is on the northern slopes of the Caucasus no hybridization has been found but on the southern slopes hybrids are known. Perhaps a strong male of one species, unable to obtain a harem of his own, drives off a weaker male of the other species and takes over his harem. Even so, the hybrids are only of the first generation, there is no continuing hybrid population. So, although the two species do hybridize, it is only as the horse and ass will hybridize to give mules, which are infertile.

From this and other evidence too detailed to give here it seems reasonable to believe that the seven kinds of ibex enumerated below are all natural species.

class	**Mammalia**
order	**Artiodactyla**
family	**Bovidae**
genus & species	***Capra aegagrus*** *bezoar goat* ***C. caucasica*** *Kuban tur* ***C. cylindricornis*** *Daghestan tur* ***C. ibex*** *alpine ibex* ***C. nubiana*** *Nubian ibex* ***C. pyrenaica*** *Spanish ibex* ***C. sibirica*** *Siberian ibex* ***C. walie*** *walia*

△ *Portrait of a Siberian ibex. The strength of the knurled horns establishes rank in males.*

▽ *Summit conference: male alpine ibexes size each other up from respective stone pillars.*

R Van Nostrand

Roebild

Ibis

Ibises belong to the same order as herons and flamingos, and have similar long spindly legs, long necks and long bills. Their necks and bills are, however, generally stouter than those of herons and the bills are down-curved. They also lack the powder-down patches of the herons. The smallest is the glossy ibis, about the size of a curlew, with a dark plumage that shines with iridescent greens and purples. It is wide-ranging, being found in southern Europe and Asia, the East Indies, Australia, parts of Africa and Madagascar, and around the Caribbean. It occasionally wanders to the British Isles. The sacred ibis is white with a black head and neck and a black 'bustle' of feathers over the tail as in cranes (p 562). In flight the dark wingtips are prominent. It lives in Africa south of the Sahara, Madagascar and Arabia. The scarlet ibis lives in tropical America from Venezuela to Brazil and the white ibis, wholly white except for red on the bill and the naked skin on the face, ranges from southern United States, where it is called the white curlew, to northern South America. These are the best known of the 25 or so species of ibis. The hermit ibis used to breed in Central Europe but has been extinct there for three centuries. The Japanese crested ibis is extremely rare. In 1966 nine were known in Japan, but the numbers in Manchuria, China and Korea are not known. The wood ibises belong to the stork family, although the name of the African wood ibis is **Ibis ibis.**

△ *Unique photograph of a bald ibis* **Geronticus calvus**. *Only about 1 000 of these birds exist, in the mountains of South Africa.* ▽ *Toes splayed, a scarlet ibis perches, stork-like, on one leg.*

Peter Johnson

John Tashjian at San Diego Zoo

Picturesque birds

Ibises along with other long-legged and long-necked birds such as herons, cranes, flamingos and storks are among the most beautiful of birds. Their plumage is often magnificent, especially when they are seen in huge flocks. Their poise is statuesque and their flight rhythmically graceful. When roosting on the bare limbs of trees, ibises are heraldic, especially when silhouetted, and scarlet ibises perched in the trees in the evening are an unbelievably magnificent sight. They look like huge blossoms caught in the rays of the setting sun. In flight a group of ibises beat their wings in unison and then glide, the front of the flock stopping first and those behind following suit, so ripples of gliding and wing-beating pass down the column.

Sacred chimney sweep

Ibises live in marshes, shallow lakes and along the shore where they feed on small water animals, such as frogs, fish, worms and small reptiles. The hermit ibis lives in the much drier country of North Africa and the Middle East, where it feeds on beetles and other small land animals. In South Africa the sacred ibis is called the 'chimney sweep' because it eats carrion and 'sweeps' out the insides of carcases for the insects feeding there. These carrion-eating habits were known in mediaeval times. In the 12th century bestiary translated by TH White it is said that the ibis 'enjoys eating corpses and snakes' eggs' and that it looks for 'little dead fish or other bodies which have been thrown up by the waves.'

Trees essential for nesting

Ibises build nests in trees, except for the hermit ibis that nests on cliffs, and the sacred ibis sometimes nests on the ground. The Japanese crested ibis nests in tall forest trees. One reason for its decline is the cutting down of forests, for even if the nesting tree is left intact while the surrounding trees are cut down the ibis will desert it. This species is unusual in that it nests in pine trees. The nests are untidy platforms of sticks and rushes, like herons' nests. The black ibis of India sometimes uses the abandoned nests of birds of prey. This ibis nests in groups of 2 or 3 pairs but the scarlet ibis nests in colonies sometimes 10 000 strong. The colonies are often shared with other birds such as cormorants, herons and egrets. Such concentrations are now much rarer as the scarlet ibis has been slaughtered for its beautiful feathers as well as for its meat.

Both parents incubate the 3 or 4 white or blue eggs, which are sometimes marked with brown, for 3 weeks. When the parents swap places at the nest they indulge in billing and cooing, preening each other and calling quietly. The chicks are fed by regurgitation, placing their bills in their parents'. When a couple of weeks old the young leave the nest and climb out onto the nearby branches. They have two coats of down before growing their dark immature plumage. Adult plumage is attained in 1—2 years.

The sacred ibis

At one time the sacred ibis bred along the banks of the Nile and the Ancient Egyptians held it in great esteem, identifying it with the god Thoth who recorded the life of every man. In pictures Thoth is shown with the head of an ibis and ibises were tamed and kept as pets in temples. They were also mummified and buried in the tombs of Pharaohs—perhaps to record their final voyage to the next world?

It is often amusing to inquire why an animal is held in veneration or to investigate its appearance in folklore. The Ancient Egyptians venerated several animals, including crocodiles and cats (see p 390), as well as ibises. Herodotus thought the high esteem accorded to the sacred ibis was due to the toll it took of venomous snakes, but perhaps a more reasonable explanation is that the ibis appeared in Egypt at the time of the all-important annual rising of the Nile, feeding and nesting on the newly flooded land then flying away as the waters subsided. It therefore became associated, together with the flooding of the Nile, with the source of life.

Extinct in Egypt, where it was once held in high reverence, the sacred ibis is by no means endangered; it is still a common bird south of the Sahara. Below: a sacred ibis planes in to join a group in the treetops with herons and a cormorant.

class	**Aves**
order	**Ciconiiformes**
family	**Threskiornithidae**
genera & species	**Eudocimus albus** *white ibis* **E. ruber** *scarlet ibis* **Geronticus eremita** *hermit ibis* **Nipponia nippon** *Japanese ibis* **Plegadis falcinellus** *glossy ibis* **Pseudibis papillosa** *black ibis* **Threskiornis aethiopica** *sacred ibis* *others*

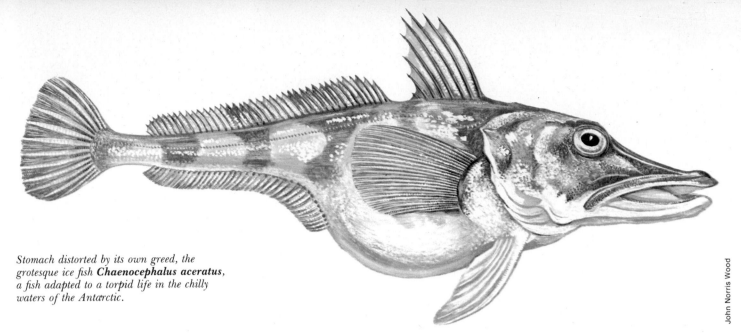

*Stomach distorted by its own greed, the grotesque ice fish **Chaenocephalus aceratus**, a fish adapted to a torpid life in the chilly waters of the Antarctic.*

John Norris Wood

Ice fish

The first reports of ice fish were made by Norwegian whalers working in the Antarctic, who brought back stories of 'bloodless' fishes they caught near their shore factories. The fishes do, in fact, have blood but it is almost transparent with a just perceptible yellowish tint. It lacks haemoglobin, the red pigment that in many other animals carries oxygen from the lungs or gills to other parts of the body. The problem of how these fishes survive without the oxygen-carrying capacity of haemoglobin has led to speculation ever since the fish were discovered but only in the last few years has it been possible, in the remoteness of the Antarctic, to carry out the necessary detailed work for its solution.

The name ice fish was given by British whalers in allusion to the translucent appearance of the body. Ice fish have no scales and the body is very pale brown or white, and slimy. A third (and also descriptive) name is crocodile fish. The front of the head is drawn out into a beak with a large, gaping mouth edged with thick lips. The eyes are large and goggling. The dorsal fin has two parts; the front part in the middle of the back is sail-like and the second part is ribbon-like, similar to the anal fin on the underside. The pectoral fins form paddles just behind the gills and the fleshy leg-like pelvic fins lie in front of them under the belly.

*There are about 18 species of ice fish, all but one of them confined to the Southern Ocean. The exception ranges north as far as Patagonia. The largest ice fish **Chaenocephalus aceratus** measures up to 2 ft long and can weigh 2½ lb.*

Sluggish carnivore

The fishes of the Antarctic are now being studied intensively by scientists of several nations but by comparison with other kinds like the Antarctic cod (p 60) little is known of the habits of the ice fish. It has recently been caught with nets at depths of about 200 ft, in some numbers, and so more is likely to be known about it soon. Its muscles are weak and its ribs soft which suggest that the fish is not active. It probably spends much of its time on the sea bed resting on its leg-like pelvic fins, engulfing passing fish or picking up carrion. Like large snakes such as the anaconda (p 41), it probably has big meals at long intervals. The large mouth can close over a fair-sized Antarctic cod and the stomach and skin of its belly can stretch to accommodate a large meal. The proof of this is that ice fishes are sometimes caught when they have engulfed an Antarctic cod already hooked. Ice fish also catch krill, the crustaceans that abound in the cold, oxygen-rich waters, supporting whales and many other Antarctic creatures.

Breeding in the Antarctic autumn

Ice fish spawn in the Antarctic autumn, between mid-March and late April. Each fish lays about 2 000 large yolky eggs, ⅙ in. in diameter, on the sea floor.

Oxygen problems

The discovery that ice fishes have no haemoglobin in their blood posed several questions. The first was how they manage to transport oxygen to their tissues, for in red blood 90% of the oxygen taken into the body is carried by the haemoglobin and the rest is dissolved in the blood plasma. Ice fishes must carry all their oxygen in the plasma and they must be able to live on very little oxygen. They are helped by the high concentration of oxygen in the Antarctic seas. One of the reasons for the vast amount of plant and animal life in the Southern Ocean, which will be referred to in the article on krill, is that gases dissolve in cold water better than in warm water. As a result the organisms living in the cold seas, where temperatures rarely rise more than a few degrees above freezing point, have a greater supply of oxygen and they oxygenate their bodies more efficiently. Ice fishes are probably able to absorb oxygen through the skin as well as through the gills.

Despite these advantages, ice fish must still absorb less oxygen than other Antarctic fish and it was presumed that this ties them to their sluggish existence. Recent experiments, however, have shown that, weight for weight, ice fish use as much oxygen in their bodies as do Antarctic cod. Some ice fishes and Antarctic cod were caught alive and put in sealed, water-filled containers. Samples of water were drawn off at intervals and the amount of oxygen in them analysed to find out how much the fish were using. It turned out that the ice fish were using as much oxygen as the Antarctic cod, so they do not seem to be labouring at a disadvantage but have a system for carrying quite enough oxygen for their sluggish way of life. The haemoglobin of the Antarctic cod would seem, then, to be an unnecessary luxury, and this may be the case for other fish. Goldfish, for instance, are able to survive indefinitely when their haemoglobin has been put out of action by carbon monoxide.

Ice fishes also have large hearts, about three times the size of the hearts of red-blooded fishes. This must enable them to pump blood very rapidly through the body and so compensate for the small amount of oxygen in the blood. A similar adaptation is found in people living in the rarefied atmosphere of high mountains.

The absence of haemoglobin in the blood of ice fish and the discovery that in other fish haemoglobin appears to be superfluous, raises awkward questions. One can ask either why ice fish lost their haemoglobin, or why so many other fishes have haemoglobin. Even when we know more about the habits and physiology of the fish, these questions may remain debatable.

class	**Pisces**
order	**Perciformes**
family	**Chaenichthyidae**
genus & species	***Chaenocephalus aceratus*** *others*

Ichneumon

This is the name used—usually in a rather imprecise way—for certain small wasps whose larvae live as parasites in the bodies of other insects. They are often referred to as 'ichneumon flies', but 'ichneumon wasp' is a better term since they belong to the insect order Hymenoptera and not to the true flies, or Diptera. Also, the term is often applied to all the parasitic Hymenoptera, including the chalcid and some of the cynipid wasps which we have already described, the cynipids under 'gall wasp'.

The name is restricted here to the superfamily Ichneumonoidea, comprising two main families, the Ichneumonidae and Braconidae.

The word 'ichneumon' has a curious history. The Ancient Egyptians regarded with favour a four-legged animal which helped to destroy crocodiles by digging up and eating their eggs. This story found its way into the early Greek literature, and they used the word 'ichneumon', meaning 'tracker', for the animal. It is generally supposed to have been the mongoose, but this is pure conjecture. It is really more likely to have been a large lizard, the Nile monitor; no clear distinction was made between beasts and reptiles in the confused zoology of ancient times.

A living death

Often the butterfly or moth collector finds a partly grown caterpillar of some particular species he wishes to have, brings it to full growth by careful feeding and is happy to see it pupate, apparently in good health. He may yet be disappointed, however, by the appearance from the pupa of a four-winged 'fly' instead of the beautiful moth or butterfly he was hoping for.

What led to this disappointment was that some time before he discovered the caterpillar, it had been found by a female ichneumon wasp. Having made sure, in some way we do not fully understand, that the caterpillar had not already been visited by another ichneumon wasp, she laid an egg on or under its skin. The caterpillar probably reared up and thrashed about when the wasp settled on it, but once the operation was over it resumed its feeding and growing in an apparently normal way. Meanwhile the egg of the ichneumon hatched into a tiny grub, which then began feeding and growing at the expense of the caterpillar's tissues.

When the time came for the caterpillar to pupate, it was harbouring a parasite of fair size in its body, but not large enough to have destroyed the working of any of its essential organs. As soon as the change to a chrysalis was completed, however, the grub began to grow apace, soon killing its host. It then turned into a pupa itself within the empty shell that should contain a moth. Some time later the ichneumon wasp hatched by splitting the skin of its own pupal covering, and then chewed its way out through the shell of the chrysalis. A moth or butterfly pupa that

△ *Living larder: with ovipositor about to leave an egg, this beetle larva is doomed.*
◁ *With sharp ovipositor, a female **Rhyssa persuasoria** pierces wood to lay an egg on the larva of a wood-boring beetle (8 × life size).*

has harboured an ichneumon is never split open as it is when it completes its transformation; it has a hole in the side.

If the hatching ichneumon is a female, she finds a male of her own species, mates and then, if summer is nearly over, probably hibernates through the winter. Next spring she will seek out another caterpillar, possibly but not necessarily of the same species that provided her with a living food supply.

No escaping the ichneumon

The very common large rusty-red ichneumon wasps of the genus *Ophion* have this sort of life history, but variations on the theme are numerous. Not all ichneumons parasitize the larvae of moths and butterflies; some attack saw-flies, some beetles, bugs or even spiders, and one sort crawls under the water to lay its eggs on the larvae of caddis-flies. Aphids are also heavily attacked by a small braconid ichneumon called *Aphidius*. The largest British ichneumon *Rhyssa persuasoria* lays eggs on the wood-boring larvae of the big saw-flies called horntails *Sirex* which burrow in pine trees, ruining their timber. The female *Rhyssa* has a very long slender ovipositor—the egg-laying organ—and with this she is able to bore through a couple of inches of solid wood and implant an egg on the horntail grub inside the trunk. The drilling through the wood is a remarkable performance, but the finding and exact locating of the larva within is even more so. Here again we do not really know what sense is employed.

Parasites on parasites

Some ichneumons lay not one, but a number of eggs, resulting in a brood of 100 or more crawling grubs inside the unhappy caterpillar. This multiple parasitisation is characteristic of the Braconidae, most of which are very small insects. One of these *Apanteles glomeratus* is a serious (from our point of

view useful) enemy of cabbage white butterflies. In this case the larvae of the ichneumon emerge from the body of the caterpillar just at the time when it has found a place to pupate. On emergence through the caterpillar's skin each ichneumon larva spins a little yellow cocoon, like a tiny replica of that of a silkworm. These little clusters of cocoons are common objects on walls surrounding vegetable gardens. If you collect these carefully and breed them out you will get quantities of *Apanteles* and also, probably, numbers of another even smaller ichneumon. The females of this species are expert at finding butterfly caterpillars infested with *Apanteles* larvae and laying eggs on the parasites, probing through the caterpillar's skin to do so. The word 'hyperparasite' is used to describe this sort of parasite within a parasite.

The stage at which the parasites emerge from the host's body can vary; it may be before pupation or after. The stage at which the eggs are laid may also vary. In the true ichneumons it is usually in the larva, but some of the minute chalcid wasps lay their eggs and complete their metamorphoses in the eggs of the host, and one is known which lays in the newly formed pupa.

Both ichneumon and chalcid wasps (see p 408) have been used in biological control of harmful insects. In New Zealand *Sirex* was accidentally introduced in imported timber and multiplied rapidly, becoming a serious pest in the pine forests and plantations. There is no ichneumon native to New Zealand that can reach it in its burrow in the tree trunks, and so in 1928 and 1929 over a thousand pupae of the big ichneumon wasp *Rhyssa persuasoria* were sent to New Zealand and the insects were released in the pine woods when they emerged. More were sent in 1931 and they all thrived. Horntails are far less abundant.

Parasites or not?

A truly parasitic animal, such as a tapeworm, does not kill the host in which it feeds. On the contrary, it is in its interest for the host to stay alive as long as possible, since if it dies the parasite perishes with it. The association of the ichneumon larva with the caterpillar in which it feeds is quite different. Here the host is doomed to die before it reaches maturity from the moment the egg is deposited in it. Ichneumon wasps really prey on caterpillars, their larvae slowly eating them alive instead of killing them immediately as a normal predator does. For this reason some authorities object to the term parasite to describe ichneumons and call them parasitoids.

phylum	**Arthopoda**
class	**Insecta**
order	**Hymenoptera**
family	**Braconidae**
genera & species	***Apanteles glomeratus*** ***Aphidius***
family	**Ichneumonidae**
genera & species	***Ophion*** ***Rhyssa persuasoria*** *others*

Iguana

The iguana family contains lizards such as the anole, the basilisk, the horned toad and many others, some of which are called iguanas in everyday English. The marine iguana is discussed under a separate heading; here we are dealing with the green iguana, the ground iguana, the land iguanas and the desert iguana or crested lizard.

The ground iguana is one of the most primitive members of the family. It has a crest like the teeth in a comb running down its back starting behind the head and petering out in the middle of the heavy tail. One kind, the rhinoceros iguana, has two or three hornlike scales on its head and a large swelling on either side of the chin. Ground iguanas reach a length of 4 ft, 2 ft shorter than the green iguana which has been introduced to the Virgin Isles and the Lesser Antilles where it has driven out the ground iguana. The native home of the green iguana is Central and northern South America. It is pale green in colour, has a crest similar to that of the ground iguana and an erectable sac under the throat. The males are larger than the females, their crests are longer and their bodies are more orange or yellow compared with the females' light green. The males also have a row of pores on the underside of each thigh, whose function is unknown.

The desert iguana lives in the deserts of North America. It measures 1 ft and is cream coloured with brown or black lines and spots. The land iguana of the Galapagos islands grows up to 5 ft. It is yellow with brown spots on the sides and legs.

High diver

The green iguana is an agile climber and adults are rarely found far from the trees of the tropical forests in which they live. It can scramble from one tree to another providing the twigs are interlaced to give reasonable support for iguanas cannot leap far. Green iguanas will, however, throw themselves from a branch 40–50 ft up and land on the ground unhurt, sprinting away to the undergrowth with barely a pause for breath. For an animal that appears so clumsy, with a heavy tail and legs splayed sideways, an iguana is remarkably fast and is extremely difficult to catch. Its reflexes are very rapid and unless one has nets the only way to catch an iguana is to throw oneself at it and even then a fullgrown iguana will be very hard to hold, as it can inflict nasty bites and scratches. Iguanas often take refuge in water and their favourite haunts are in trees overhanging pools and rivers. If disturbed they leap from the branch where they were lying and dive into the water. They swim underwater, propelling themselves with their tails, and surface under cover of vegetation along the bank.

▷ *The Barrington Island iguana of the Galapagos* **Conolophus pallidus**. *Local people prize its flesh, goats destroy its home. Only 300 remain.*

John Markham

Brosset: Jacana

◁◁ *The aptly named rhinoceros iguana, with two horn-like scales on the top of its nose.*
◁ *A green iguana pauses, throat sac down and crest erect, to fight or flee an intruder, its partly missing tail witness of a past escape.*

The green iguana comes down to the ground in cold weather and hides under logs or in holes, but the other iguanas are usually ground-living and only occasionally climb trees. The desert iguana is a very fast runner and races about on its hindlegs.

Vegetarian lizards

As adults green iguanas eat a variety of plant foods, including young shoots, fruits, flowers and leaves, but the young ones also eat insects. Other iguanas are also vegetarian. The desert iguana prefers the yellow-flowered creosote bush but also eats other flowers, and after the flowering season is over it eats insects and carrion. Land iguanas feed on cactus and the larger species eat small rodents.

Eggs and constant temperature

Male land iguanas of the Galapagos form territories which they defend against other males. Each keeps watch from a rock and if another male intrudes he climbs down from his vantage point, walks slowly over to his rival and displays at him, pointing his snout at the sky and jerking his head up and down. If this does not scare the intruder into running away a fight breaks out, each trying to grab the loose skin on the other's flanks.

The female land iguanas live in the same burrows as their mates or in separate burrows alongside. Iguanas generally lay their eggs in nests well separated from each other but on a small island in Panama green iguanas were found nesting in great numbers close together on a sandy beach. Each female spent up to 2 weeks on the shore. For the first few days she probed the sand and dug small holes seeking a suitable site. Then she dug a large burrow 1—2 yd long and 2—3 ft deep. Because the beach was so crowded some were seen digging up other nests and scattering the eggs. Eggs were laid at the bottom of the burrow which was filled in afterwards. The females spent some time filling the hole and at the same time filling in adjacent holes. Sometimes this meant filling in the burrows of other females who might be trapped and buried.

The green iguana lays 20—70 eggs in a ▬▬▬ The eggs are spherical, white and about 1½ in. diameter. They hatch in 3 months and it has been found that an almost constant temperature is needed for their development. A few degrees too high or too low and they fail to hatch. Although the female abandons her eggs after they are laid she ensures their survival by burying them in a suitable part of the beach. She chooses a spot where the temperature fluctuates only 1°—2° either side of 30°C/86°F. The young iguanas measure about 10 in. when they hatch and grow to 3 ft in one year.

Fooling the iguanas

Man and his domestic animals are the iguanas' worst enemies. Their flesh is relished in many parts of the world. Hawks

are also serious enemies, for they catch iguanas as they lie basking in trees. In parts of South America iguanas are hunted by men imitating the screams of hawks. The iguanas' reaction to the cries is to 'freeze' and they are then easily caught. Snakes also hunt iguanas; a 6 ft boa constrictor has been found with an adult green iguana in its stomach.

Vanishing iguanas

When Charles Darwin visited the Galapagos islands in 1835 land iguanas were extremely abundant. Darwin wrote 'I cannot give a more forcible proof of their numbers than by stating that when we were left at James Island, we could not for some time find a spot free from their burrows to pitch our single tent.' Since then man has settled on the island, bringing with him dogs, cats, pigs, rats, goats and other animals and the iguana population is now a fraction of its former size. On some islands, however, where there are no goats, there are still large numbers of iguanas. The link between goats and iguanas is that goats strip the vegetation, depriving iguanas of cover. Some islands seem to be populated by adult iguanas only. They can survive in the open but young iguanas need cover to protect them from the Galapagos hawk. Without this cover they are killed off, and when the old lizards die there will be none left.

△ *Flowers on the menu: although it eats mainly insects when young, this green iguana seems to be interested in the more adult diet of tender young buds. They often clamber in trees.*

class	**Reptilia**	
order	**Squamata**	
suborder	**Sauria**	
family	**Iguanidae**	
genera & species	***Conolophus subcristatus*** land iguana	
	Cyclura cornuta *rhinoceros iguana*	
	Dipsosaurus dorsalis *desert iguana*	
	Iguana iguana *green iguana*	

Impala

The impala is one of the most graceful of the antelopes. About 30–40 in. high, weighing 140–160 lb, it is chestnut brown with a lighter brown area on the flanks and a sharply defined white belly. The male has lyre-shaped, ribbed horns, 20–30 in. long, which make one spiral turn; the female is hornless. The neck and limbs are slender and delicate. The impala occupies a rather isolated position in the family Bovidae. In the past there have been divided opinions on whether it was more nearly related to the gazelles or to the reedbuck. Recently Alan Gentry has suggested, on a study of the skull, teeth and horn-cores, that the impala is more nearly related to the hartebeest and gnu.

Taking to cover

Impala inhabit a wide area of East and South Africa. They seem to like being near water and they avoid open country, being more usually found where there are low trees and tall shrubs, without much ground cover, in scrub and thornbush country especially. Their distribution is patchy because they do not venture much into either overgrown or open land. So, although abundant in most of the Kruger National Park, they are absent from much of its northern end.

△ Poise in triplicate: a female impala trio nose down in their local river. Impala seldom stray far from water, and will not venture into arid surroundings or bushy thickets.

According to its suitability for the impala, an area may have a density of anything from seven to over 200 per square mile; the usual figure is 50–70. Concentrations are highest in the dry season, as with most African ungulates; this also happens to be the time of the rut. In the wet season, impala are more scattered, and occupy small home ranges; but they may wander as much as 15 miles for water.

Impala both graze and browse, but in most areas they eat mainly grass.

1133

Born when the grass sprouts

The rut takes place in the beginning of the dry season. The lambs are born, one to each ewe, after a gestation of 180–210 days, early in the wet season when there is most food for them.

In Rhodesia, the first lambs are dropped in early December and the peak of lambing is from December 15 to January 1. Two-year-old ewes, breeding for the first time, give birth later in the season than older ones. The young grow rapidly—in young males the horns begin to sprout in late February—and are usually weaned before the next rut, at which time they may form separate bands. In the rut nearly all ewes breed, at least 97% of the older ones, and 85% of the two-year-olds.

The rut begins when the males set up their territories in late May or early June. Surplus rams attach themselves to small groups of ewes, and the yearlings form small bands by themselves. The ewes live in herds the year round. At the end of the lambing season these may number (including lambs) as much as 100. At Fort Tuli, Rhodesia, herds of 200–300 have been counted. These large herds stay together from January to May, and only a few males associate with them; then in May they break into smaller groups, which pass through the rams' territories and are covered by them. After the rut, the ram groups reform but groups of mixed sex and age predominate. By December, the groups are reduced in size to ten or less; the ewes become secretive, separating off for a while to give birth.

The main predator is probably the leopard. Existing populations of impala are often subject to poaching, but this does not severely affect their numbers.

△ *The roving eye: a handsome male runs a casual glance over the scrubland.*
▷ *A herd of mothers and lambs straddles a road. Males join them only for the rut.*
▽ *Poetry in motion: female in full flight.*

Switchback fugitives

Impala rams become quite aggressive in the rutting season, especially when setting up territories. At this time, fighting and chasing are common. The rams, once the territories are set up, leave their bases to drink at the waterholes, which are a no-man's-land. But the most conspicuous piece of impala behaviour is their alarm reaction. When disturbed, the whole group indulge in a magnificent display of leaping. They jump forward, straight up or with side turns, as much as 10 ft into the air, up and down, round and in all directions. What is the function of this behaviour? It has been suggested that in reality its purpose is to confuse a predator, such as a big cat who is trying to single out one animal from the group it is attacking. The leaping impala, helped by their contrasting colours, seem to be wholly successful in preventing this, and completely confuse the attacker.

A number of animals show this sort of behaviour when alarmed by a predator. Instead of putting as much ground between themselves and their adversary they jink to and fro to cause confusion. The jinking of hares is an example that readily comes to mind and it has been suggested that continually changing direction prevents an enemy from cutting off its prey.

class	**Mammalia**
order	**Artiodactyla**
family	**Bovidae**
genus & species	**Aepyceros melampus**

Indian buffalo

The buffaloes are a distinctive group of cattle. They are stockily built with large hoofs and large shaggy ears. The horns are triangular in cross-section instead of oval or circular like those of true cattle and bison. The head is carried horizontally and the muzzle is broad and hairless. The back is straight but slopes down towards the hindquarters. The hair is sparse. The two genera of buffaloes are **Syncerus**, the Cape buffalo of Africa (p 360) and **Bubalus** the Indian or water buffalo of Asia.

The Asiatic buffaloes differ from the Cape buffalo in the shape of the skull, in the horns, and the forward-lying hair in the middle of the back. The Indian buffalo is by far the largest of the Asiatic buffaloes and is an important domestic animal, noted for its docility, in contrast with the aggressiveness of its wild relatives. It is 5–6 ft in height and weighs $\frac{1}{2}$–1 ton. It

is black in the wild but the domesticated animal may be grey, black, pink or white with white spots on the chin, throat and limbs. The horns are semicircular, spreading out sideways and then backward, in a line with the back. There are localised populations of wild Indian buffaloes in Ceylon, Nepal, Assam, Indo-China and Borneo. A smaller species is the tamarau, restricted to the island of Mindoro in the Philippines. It is only $3\frac{1}{2}$ ft high with short, thick horns which turn mainly backwards and are only slightly semi-circular. It is jet black with a few white spots, very bull-necked and weighs 600–700 lb. In historic times, the tamarau occurred on Luzon as well as Mindoro.

The other two Asiatic buffaloes, known as anoas, are found only on the island of Celebes. They are small and rather antelope-like with short, conical backward-pointing horns and more slender necks. The lowland anoa, the larger, is about

$3\frac{1}{2}$ ft high, black, with white spots on jaw, throat and legs. The mountain anoa is about 2–3 ft in height, with shorter tail and horns, golden to dark brown in colour with no white marks except a few white spots above the hoofs. The hair in both is long, soft and woolly. Although these have always been treated as separate species it is now thought that the two are just variants of the same species, and that the tamarau is really a dwarfed island form of the big Indian buffalo.

Shy but pugnacious cattle

Wild buffaloes are so unapproachable that their way of life has not been studied in any detail. In the Kaziranga Game Reserve, in Assam, where there are about 400 wild Indian buffalo, they live in herds of 10–20, in swampy regions and grass jungle, where the elephant grass grows 10–15 ft high. The tamarau is more solitary, but has been seen

▽ Buffalo bath: a contented soak, away from the intense heat of the tropical sun.

associating in groups of up to eleven. It inhabits rugged country, on the forest borders and in bamboo. Recently it has become scarce as the forest and bamboo is cut down, and perhaps only 200 or so now survive. It is often shot by cattle farmers. As recently as 1964, tamarau could be seen grazing in the open in morning and evening, but today they have become more nocturnal.

Cattle harems
The wild bulls of the Indian buffalo round up the cows into harems, they then become particularly aggressive. Both the wild and the domesticated animals may breed all the year round, but in the wild there is a breeding peak that occurs at different times, in different areas. In Asia most of the young are born between October and December, after a gestation of 310 days.

In Europe, for example, in Italy where there are semi-wild Indian buffaloes, the young are born between February and April. Buffalo become sexually mature at 2–3 years and in Italy, they often breed at this age, but in parts of the Far East, such as

Cambodia, the domesticated animals may not mature until they are about 5 years old, either because they are prevented from doing so or because the poor feed they get delays maturity. Physical maturity does not come until $3\frac{1}{2}$ to 4 years.

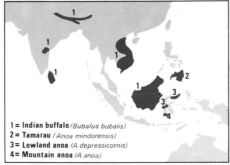

1 = **Indian buffalo** (*Bubalus bubalis*)
2 = **Tamarau** (*Anoa mindorensis*)
3 = **Lowland anoa** (*A. depressicornis*)
4 = **Mountain anoa** (*A. anoa*)

◁▽ *Aggressive cousin: the anoa of Celebes has a well-founded vicious reputation—it will even kill other animals enclosed with it.*
▽▷ *Beast of all work: an Indian buffalo being used to thresh a pile of corn.*
▽▽ *Mother and child, cool in flooded pasture.*

Domestic Indian buffaloes, bred partly at least for milk, have a long, overdeveloped lactation, like domestic cattle. In India and Pakistan they give 40–50% of the countries' milk. In these countries, people tend to buy a female buffalo for a small sum, keep her for one or two lactations, and then get rid of her, since they cannot afford to keep a herd. Meat is forbidden to Hindus but, unlike the humped cattle or zebu, buffalo are not in themselves sacred. Males used for draught are often castrated, and commonly the tail is cut off as well. About half the old animals provide meat for non-Hindus.

Man—the worst enemy
Wild Indian buffaloes may occasionally be preyed on by tigers, but in general they have no serious enemies except man. Anoas live on an island quite free of carnivorous mammals which might prey on them, but they have, nevertheless, a reputation for being extremely aggressive. In captivity they cannot be kept with any other large animals as they will stab them in the belly with their short horns.

Cyr Colour Agency

Peter Hill

Tomsich: Bavaria

Widespread buffalo

The domestic buffalo, usually known as the water buffalo, is one of man's most important and widespread servants. Various breeds are classified as either swamp or river buffaloes. Swamp buffaloes can work in marshy land and humid jungle. They are stocky, heavy creatures, very strong, but have the drawback that they suffer in hot sun, and must bathe or wallow regularly. They are used on a large scale as draught animals in the rice-fields of Malaysia, Indonesia, Indo-China, southern China and the Philippines, where they are called kerabau or carabao. River buffaloes are more specialised, preferring dry pastures, and clear rivers and canals. Used especially in India and Pakistan, they are very docile, and are kept for their milk.

There are about 78 million domestic buffaloes in the world. Over half are in India, with about 10 million in southern China and 5 million in Pakistan. The milk-giving river buffalo of India has been fairly recently introduced into southeast Asia, and is gradually replacing the swamp-buffalo although it is not such a good worker. The present distribution of domesticated buffaloes is of very long standing: in the Philippines, for example, they were there well before the Spaniards arrived.

Domestic buffaloes are also found in smaller numbers in Europe, North Africa and West Asia: in, Turkey, Iraq, Syria,

Transcaucasia, the Lenkoran plain in the south of Soviet Azerbaijan, Egypt, Eritrea, Greece, Bulgaria, Hungary, Rumania, Yugoslavia, Italy and Andalusia (Spain). In Egypt, they were unknown in the time of the Pharaohs and were probably introduced there in the 9th century AD via Iraq and Syria. Now there are 1¼ million in Egypt. It was only in 1933 that a small number were taken from Egypt to Eritrea.

The European domestic buffalo is of a type very close to the Surti breed of Gujerat, Bombay and Baroda in Western India. Buffalo were probably introduced into Italy from Hungary in the 6th century AD. In 1900, there were 50 000 there; in 1930, only 15 000; now there are still fewer. The draining of the Pontine Marshes has mainly eliminated the buffalo, besides which their state of domestication was never as close as it is in India or the Far East, and the Italian buffaloes, in effect semi-wild, were considered rather dangerous. From Italy, they have been introduced into Guyana, Cayenne, Trindidad, and Brazil; also into the lower Congo.

From the island of Timor—where at present there are 90 000 buffaloes but only 4 000 true cattle—three buffalo were imported to Melville Island, North Australia, in 1825. In 1827, a further fifteen were taken there, and in 1829 another sixteen. They were released on the island to serve as food for settlers and aborigines. In 1838 a few

△ *Indian buffaloes pause to graze on their journey from a working site. Buffaloes are the mainstay of most of Asia's agriculture—they are even bred to suit varying terrain.*

from Melville Island were introduced to the vicinity of Port Essington, and have since spread south to the swamps and grasslands of the Mary, Adelaide and Alligator rivers, and west to the Darwin coast. Some also got ashore from a shipwreck on the Ord river, in Kimberleys district. So, in 1885 there were 6 000 on Melville Island and 60 000 on the mainland of Australia. They have certainly contributed, by overgrazing, to the present scarcity of most Australian indigenous fauna even if they have made their contribution in the form of good leather from their hides. They also provide meat for a few of the aborigines and white hunters in the coastal districts.

class	**Mammalia**
order	**Artiodactyla**
family	**Bovidae**
genus & species	**Anoa anoa** mountain anoa **A. depressicornis** lowland anoa **A. mindorensis** tamarau **Bubalus bubalis** Indian buffalo

Jacana

These are water birds that look like long-legged coots, but are in fact waders related to the curlew, avocet and snipe. Jacana is a Spanish word derived from the name given to the birds by South American Indians. In English the soft 'c' is usually pronounced as 'k'. Lily-trotter, lotus-bird and water-walker are alternative names, and describe the jacana's habit of walking on floating vegetation, supported on extremely long toes. On the 'wrist' of the wing there is a knob or spike sometimes 1 in. long. This is said to be used in fighting.

There are seven species of jacana living in America, Africa south of the Sahara and including Madagascar, Asia from India to the Malay Archipelago and in eastern Australia. The American jacana is found in Mexico and the West Indies south to northern Argentina. Its plumage is reddish-brown with yellow-green undersides to the wings. Some American jacanas have completely black plumage or a black head. They have a yellow frontal shield like that of coots. The Australian lotus-bird, which is also found in the East Indies, is brownish with black on the chest and back of the neck and white on the throat and under the tail. The white patch on the throat is bordered with orange and there is a shield of scarlet. Most jacanas have very short tails but in the breeding season the pheasant-tailed jacana, of India to the Philippines, grows a long, curving tail of black feathers. The rest of the plumage is brown with white on the head and neck except for a golden patch on the neck surrounded by a band of black.

Walking on water

Jacanas are found on ponds, lakes and slow-moving rivers where there are abundant waterlilies, water hyacinths and other floating plants. Outside the breeding season they may gather in flocks of hundreds or thousands. A little over 10 years ago their range in Australia moved south when aquatic plants invaded lagoons near Sydney. They can run over the soft water plants because their long toes spread their weight like snowshoes. Sometimes they appear to be running over clear water but they are being supported by perhaps two or three stems. Their gait is a dainty high-stepping, lifting the feet high so the toes clear the surface and jerking their tails at each step. Jacanas can swim but rarely do so and if pressed flutter across open water with legs and toes dangling. They feed on water plants and small animals.

Silence until the rain

Jacanas are usually silent, but in the mating season they give voice to a variety of calls: piping, churring, clucking and grunting are used by most species when breeding, with a scolding chittering when alarmed.

Like most waterfowl, they breed in the

△ The lily-trotter: an African jacana **Actophilornis africanus** uses long, widely-splayed toes to run over floating water plants. ▽ Mystery: why do jacanas flip up their wings after landing?

later stages of the rainy season. Courtship display consists of showing off the wings, weed carrying and bowing.

Floating nests

Jacana nests are extremely flimsy. The four eggs are laid on a coil of weed or a few rush stems piled together, or even on a water-lily leaf. The eggs are very glossy and look as if they are varnished. They have so much marking that the brown background is often lost. The gloss may make them un-wettable—a useful condition, as the nest may submerge as the parent steps onto it.

The adults are very much alike but the female is often larger than the male. In some species at least, the female plays little or no part in rearing the young and she may have several mates. Observations on the bronze-winged jacana of India from a floating hide revealed that both adults collected nest material but that the female took an active part in courtship and left incubation of the eggs and care of the young to the male. The male left the nest only to feed while the female stood guard, driving away moorhens and herons that came too near. Later another male arrived at the pool and, although attacked by the first male it was able to set up a territory at the far end of the pool. The female would peck the two males when they fought; she mated with the second male and laid a second clutch which he raised.

The chicks hatch out after 2 weeks or more and are able to run about immediately.

When danger threatens they lie motionless or dive under water while the parents lure the enemy away with a distraction display, attracting attention to themselves by flapping their wings and calling.

Holding the babies

Some jacanas incubate their eggs by holding them under their wings. This seems strange until it is realised that this will keep the eggs clear of the water when the jacana sits on its flimsy floating nest. The eggs are scooped up with the wings and carried two on each side. After the eggs have hatched the chicks will take refuge under their parents' wings. They raise their heads and stretch their tiny wings above their backs to invite their parent to pick them up. Jacanas have one bone in the forewing flattened to form a plate or blade, and this may help in scooping up the eggs.

class	**Aves**
order	**Charadriiformes**
family	**Jacanidae**
genera & species	**Jacana spinosa** *American jacana* **Metopidius indicus** *bronze-winged jacana* **Irediparra gallinacea** *Australian jacana* **Hydrophasianus chirurgus** *pheasant-tailed jacana others*

1139

Sven Gillsäter: Tio

Although few fossils of golden jackals have been found, suggesting a limited range in the past, jackals now live in North Africa, a large part of Asia and even in a small area of southeast Europe, partly in Russia and partly in the Balkans. The few fossils there are of the golden jackal date from the Late Pleistocene period (up to 100 000 years ago) and show that it once lived in Italy. Jackals similar to **C. aureus** lived in North Africa in the middle Pleistocene and fossils of other species of jackals have been found in Africa which date back to 3 million years ago. The distribution of the three modern species is shown on the map below. The divisions between these is obscured by the existence of many races and subspecies.

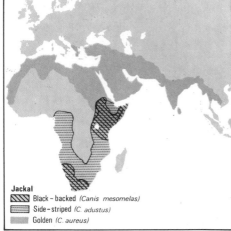

Jackal
- Black – backed (Canis mesomelas)
- Side – striped (C. adustus)
- Golden (C. aureus)

Jackal

There are three species of jackal, distinguished by their colouring. The golden or Indian jackal is a dirty yellow with black and brown hairs and has a black-tipped reddish-brown tail. The black-backed jackal is black shot with grey on its back and neck and pale underneath, there being a very distinct boundary between the two. The tail has a black tip. The side-striped jackal has a pair of light and dark stripes on each side of the body and a white-tipped tail. The jackals are alike in size; the head and body is 22 – 29 in. long and tail 9 – 14 in. and they stand about 16 in. at the shoulder.

Jackals once ranged throughout Africa, Europe and southern Asia; now they are found over most of Africa but only the golden jackal is found in Asia and southeastern Europe. Until recently it ranged as far north and west as Hungary.

No competition

Jackals live in wooded and open country and often come into towns and cities, scavanging for refuse and carrion. They are usually seen singly or in pairs, foraging mainly at night. Packs of jackals are sometimes seen but are now much rarer than they used to be. The pairs hold territories, sometimes 2 miles across, marked with urine by both sexes and defended against other jackals. Fights are rare and territorial disputes are settled by aggressive displays.

△ *Anticipation: a pair of jackal cubs await their parents' return to the termite mound den.*

In the Serengeti, black-backed and golden jackals have different habitats. Most of the black-backed jackals live in bush country while the golden jackals live on the open plains. Hence competition is reduced and where the two species do live side by side, as along the borders of the bush, a jackal will not interfere with another of a different species that wanders through its territory. There is also a separation in their feeding and breeding habits.

Not only scavengers

It used to be thought that, like hyaenas, jackals were scavengers and the name jackal was used as a term of contempt. Jackals are indeed carrion eaters and scavengers feeding on the remains of prey left by lions and leopards, but they are also hunters. Their main prey is gazelles, especially young gazelles, which they chase in a typically dog-like fashion, tiring an animal then slashing at it with their teeth. The black-backed jackals generally bite at the throat, whereas golden jackals go for the belly. The success of the attack depends very much on whether the jackal is hunting by itself or with its mate. In a study made in the Serengeti, single jackals were successful in only 16% of their attacks. Jackals working in pairs were successful in 67% of their attacks. The attacks are sometimes frustrated by female gazelles coming between the jackals and their prey, butting at the jackals and driving them away. Any food that a jackal cannot eat immediately is carried away and buried to be eaten later.

When feeding in open country, black-backed and golden jackals feed on the same food. This includes young gazelles, insects, carrion, rats, hares, ground-nesting birds, and even fruit. In South Africa jackals have become a pest of pineapple plantations and in India they eat sugar cane and ripe coffee beans. In the bush country, however, the two jackals have dissimilar diets. The black-backed jackals feed more on gazelle and the golden jackal more on insects such as termites and dung beetles.

Young born in dens

Some 2 – 7 pups are born in a burrow that the female digs herself or takes over from another animal and enlarges. Black-backed jackals often enlarge holes in termites' nests, while golden jackals convert the holes of warthogs and other animals to their own needs, often making several entrances. If disturbed, jackals carry their young to new burrows.

As is usual in the dog family there is a strong bond between the parents and both male and female bring food back for the pups. Whenever one returns there is a ritual, the pups running out with tails wagging and ears pressed back. They run alongside their parent keeping their noses just by the corner of its mouth. The parent who has been guarding the cubs also behaves in the same way and the returning parent regurgitates lumps of meat, which are snapped up by the pups or picked up by the second parent and redistributed. When the pups are 8 months old they begin to forage for themselves, catching insects, but they are dependent on their parents for another 2 months.

△ *Canine manners: a side-striped jackal seeks 'permission' to sit down.* ▽ *Not just scavengers: jackals often hunt and kill their own prey.*

The lion's lackey?

Hyaena and jackal are both used as terms of contempt for hangers-on. They are synonyms for parasites, spongers or sycophants. This unpleasant association is derived from the original idea that hyaenas and jackals were scavengers, hanging around the large carnivores for a free meal. In Shakespeare's time the jackal was described as the lion's usher or forerunner. It was believed that two or three jackals would run ahead of a lion like hounds in front of the huntsmen. They followed the scent of the prey and when finding it would bark or howl to alert the lion who would then attack. After the lion had finished eating its attendants picked over the remains.

Such stories were made up on the basis of hearing jackals howling at night and finding them around the remains of large animals at daybreak. Now that zoologists are studying animals at night, they are finding that hyaenas and jackals are hunters in their own right and that lions are not above scavenging the hyaenas' prey.

These studies have not completely cleared the jackal's name. It scavenges a great deal, especially around human settlements and is often credited with digging up bodies— its blood-curdling howl must help reinforce any ideas people may have based on the jackal's grave-robbing habits.

class	**Mammalia**	
order	**Carnivora**	
family	**Canidae**	
genus	*Canis adustus* side-striped jackal	
& species	*C. aureus* golden jackal	
	C. mesomelas black-backed jackal	

No honour among thieves: despite vicious beaks and overwhelming numbers a jackal clears its meal of vultures (above) and threatens all who come near.

Jackdaw *Corvus monedula*

Jane Burton: Photo Res

Stop thief: the jackdaw's habit of stealing bright objects is immortalised in many stories. One concerns an ex-sailor's jackdaw which would snatch lighted cigarettes from his lips and fly away.

Jackdaw

The jackdaw is a bird renowned for its talkative and thievish nature. It is familiar to many people as it spends much of its time around buildings such as church towers. It was called **monedula** *by the Romans, its Old English name was daw; in the 16th century it became known as Jack daw. The two words later became joined to make one and both daw and jackdaw were used as names of contempt for foolish, thievish and over-talkative people.*

The jackdaw is a member of the crow family. It is 13 in. long, and has black plumage shot with blue on the back and head and with a grey nape and pale blue eyes. Its short but strong bill is black and so are the legs and toes. It ranges across Europe except for the extreme north, across into northwest Africa, and into much of west and central Asia.

Sociable jackdaws

The original home of jackdaws was probably on cliffs but they readily adopted buildings when the opportunities arose, for their nooks and crannies were good substitutes for cliffs and craggy hills. By taking to buildings they also found plenty of food, especially around farms. Capacious chimneys, once fashionable, provide a good substitute for hollow trees in which jackdaws readily build their nests. They also frequent park land and cultivated land.

On the ground a jackdaw walks with a jerky, swaggering strut. Gregarious, it lives in flocks and will join flocks of its larger relatives, the rooks, whose roosts it often shares. It flies with rapid wingbeats, on a somewhat erratic course and often goes in for aerial displays, the whole flock joining in, although individual members tend to keep to pairs within the flock. While flying the characteristic call note *tchack* (or 'Jack!') is used, together with other variations on this note. The birds call in a clamour, especially in the evening when flying around a roost.

Stealing anything bright

Jackdaws feed on insects, especially grubs, and any small vertebrates as well as fruits and seeds. Chicken runs are visited for grain and other foods and jackdaws will scavenge rubbish heaps and feed from bird tables. They are virtually omnivorous and at times will rob the nests of small birds, taking eggs as well as nestlings, but tastes vary from one district to another. In one place, for example, the local jackdaws will visit cherry trees with ripening fruit day after day until the crop is gone, but in another place will ignore a similar crop. Nevertheless, ripe and highly-coloured soft fruits generally seem to be attractive and this may be linked with the birds' habit of stealing bright objects and hiding them. The habit is immortalized in many stories, from the 'Jackdaw of Rheims' to the tale of the ex-sailor whose tame jackdaw would snatch lighted cigarettes from his lips and then fly away, followed by a torrent of nautical oaths.

Like the ex-sailor, jackdaws themselves are voluble. Their native vocabulary includes a wide range of notes, many of them melodious and warbling. Jackdaws are also good mimics of many sounds, including human speech. It used to be thought that slitting a jackdaw's tongue made it a good talker and many thousands of tame jackdaws have been mutilated in this way. It makes no difference, of course, because birds do not use the tongue as we do to form words. Some jackdaws readily learn to talk, others do not, and cutting the tongue does not alter this.

Huge, messy nests in chimneys

Jackdaw courtship consists largely of the male bowing to the female and at times pressing the beak onto the breast to show off the grey head, as well as flicking the wings and jerking the tail. Both build the nest, usually no more than a small platform of sticks with a lining of wool, fur, hair, grass and paper in any kind of hole, in a tree, chimney or church tower, or in a rabbit burrow. Where there is room there may be a deep layer of sticks with the nest proper on top of it. In late April 4—6 light blue eggs with a few dark spots are laid. The female incubates for 17 days, being fed by the male. Both bring food for the young in throat pouches for 30—35 days.

Jackdaws often nest in trees reduced by age to a hollow bole. They fill this with sticks to a depth of several feet and then build a nest of fur, hair or wool on this column. In the chimney of one old house, for example, nesting jackdaws brought in so much material that sticks gradually poured out into the fireplace, covering the wide hearth as well as filling the chimney. To clear the chimney and fireplace a waggon-load of sticks had to be carted away! More surprising, a pair of jackdaws have often built in the space containing a spiral staircase, filling it with sticks.

Feathered fire-raisers

The fire service records in many parts of the world tell of firemen being called to put out fires in the upper parts of trees. In many of these the burning tree stood on its own, far from a highway and the point at which the fire started was too high for anyone to have thrown a lighted cigarette or match into it to start the fire.

Some years ago a man walking through the woods in Surrey, in the south of England, ducked his head to pass under a low bough of a yew tree and felt a burning sensation on the back of his neck. He found it was a red-hot ember and looked up to see a fire starting halfway up the tree. He ran to the nearest telephone, called the fire service and the fire was put out, but not before the upper half of the tree had been reduced to bare and blackened branches. At the point where the fire had started was a small hollow in the yew trunk containing the sticks of a jackdaw's nest. The lining was burnt to ashes. The chances are that one of the jackdaws had carried a burning cigarette to the nest.

class	**Aves**
order	**Passeriformes**
family	**Corvidae**
genus & species	*Corvus monedula*

Aquatic boxer: because of the ritualised fighting which occurs between males during the breeding season, the Jack Dempsey, when it first became popular, was named after the world heavyweight boxer. During display the large black spots become masked as other colours heighten.

Jack Dempsey

This dazzling fish once enjoyed, among aquarists, a high popularity which still persists, but to a lesser degree. It is very aggressive and can create havoc in a mixed tank, with other kinds of fishes so it needs to be kept in a separate aquarium and to be made a special pet. The fighting between males is, however, ritualized and has the appearance of a boxing match. The fish was accordingly named after the world heavyweight boxer at the time it first became popular.

Young fishes are brown but mature males, which are up to 8 in. long, are deep brown to black peppered with light blue spots, and some yellow spots, all over the body. They also have a round black spot at the centre of the body and another at the base of the tail. The upper edge of the dorsal fin is red and the iris of the eye is also red. The females are slightly smaller than the males and have fewer blue spots and shorter fins. The body of both is deep and slightly flattened sideways. The head is large, with a jutting lower jaw. The forehead of the male bulges as it gets older.

The Jack Dempsey lives in slow flowing waters of the basins of the Amazon and Rio Negro in South America.

Queensberry rules

Almost nothing is known about how the Jack Dempsey lives in its natural habitat. It has, however, been closely studied as an aquarium fish, especially in regard to its rules of fighting and its breeding. These two aspects of its behaviour are closely linked, as they are in other species of animals. When a male Jack Dempsey comes into breeding condition he establishes a territory. Should another male swim into that territory the owner faces the newcomer, swims over to him and begins what is known as a lateral display; swimming beside him so the two are nose to tail and lying alongside each other, separated by only a short distance. At the same time he raises his dorsal and anal fins, spreads his paired fins and raises his gill-covers. From the side he now looks very much bigger. At the same time his colours grow brighter, and this makes the two black spots stand out much more. The total result is that he looks much more terrifying to his opponent.

His opponent may do one of two things. He may retreat, in which event he is chased across the boundary of the territory. He may, and usually does, respond to the display by raising his own fins and his own colours grow brighter. In that event the two circle each other, trying to butt each other with the sharp edge of the jaw. The two may later seize each other by the mouth in a trial of strength. In the end it is almost invariably the intruder that finally gives up and retreats, being then chased by the owner of the territory. Slight injuries may be sustained in the fight—very occasionally these may be serious.

Feminine pacifism

Should a female wander into the territory something of the same sort takes place, but everything depends on how near she is to being ready to spawn. In any case, the male displays at her as if she were a male, but instead of raising her fins she lowers them. This indicates to him that she is a female. It is what is called a show of symbolic inferiority. It does not prevent him attacking her, butting her with his jaw, but she accepts these blows and does not fight back. In the end she leaves the territory, chased out, if she is not ready to spawn, but if she is ready to spawn the male's aggressiveness dies down and he accepts her as a mate. Given plenty of space, as they would have in the wild, a female not ready to mate would have room to get away. In a tank a female, in these circumstances, would be beaten up. The usual procedure, in bringing a male and a female together in an aquarium, is to put a sheet of glass in the tank to separate them. They do all their displaying through the glass which prevents them harming each other. In due course this turns to courtship as the female comes into breeding condition, and when the glass is finally taken out they come together peacefully as a pair to spawn.

Working off energy

'Coming into breeding condition' means more than merely getting ready to spawn. Especially in the male there is a build-up of energy which is largely dissipated in fighting. In many cichlid fishes he digs pits in the sand, as described for the firemouth (p 764). Instead of digging several small pits as some cichlids do, the Jack Dempsey digs one big pit. This is interpreted by some scientists as the result of the female taking a long time to come into breeding condition. They compare it with the way some birds build extra large nests when their mates are slow to reach mating condition.

Eventually, both male and female Jack Dempsey choose a flat surface and start cleaning it with their mouths. Then the female moves over this surface laying her eggs, the male following her and fertilising the eggs as they lie stuck to the surface. The eggs take 51 hours to hatch, during which time both parents fan them with their fins. For some 96 hours after hatching the babies are feeding on their yolk sacs, unable to swim. They are then known as wrigglers, and the parents take each wriggler in turn in their mouths and place it in a pit in the sand, where they guard their family. As the babies begin to swim out of the pit the parents pick them up in their mouths and spit them back into the mass. There comes a time, however, when the young swimmers are too big for the parents to keep spitting them back and so they give up doing so. Instead, they direct their efforts to keeping their family of several hundred bunched together for protection. Some 1 000 or more eggs may be laid in a season.

Family cannibalism

One thing scientists have tried to find out is whether Jack Dempseys recognize their own babies. They have taken away their eggs and replaced them by eggs laid by a related species. From these experiments it seems that provided the foster broods grow at the same rate and are about the same size all will be well. So it seems the Jack Dempseys are not recognizing their own babies but are recognizing that the family they are guarding are the same size and have the same growth rate as they should have. Sometimes, in swapping the clutches of eggs, the scientists have overlooked a batch of eggs on the underside of a slab of rock. When, therefore, hatching time comes the wrigglers are half Jack Dempseys and half the babies of another species. All goes well at first but after a few weeks the two sets of babies begin to differ in size, one set growing slightly more quickly than the other, and these larger babies eat their smaller foster-brethren. Although they have lived with them all the time these babies can recognize when one of their foster brothers or sisters is slightly smaller than themselves and so can be overpowered.

class	**Pisces**
order	**Perciformes**
family	**Cichlidae**
genus & species	***Cichlasoma biocellatus***

Training session: young immature 3in. Jack Dempseys circle one another in their aquarium. Almost nothing is known of their behaviour in the wild, but from observations in the aquarium their rules of fighting and their breeding are now known. These two aspects of their behaviour are closely linked as in many animal species.

Jack rabbit

The jack rabbits of the western United States are hares belonging to the genus **Lepus** — they are close relatives of the brown hare, varying hare and snowshoe rabbit (p 1019). The white-tailed jack rabbit, also known as the plains or prairie hare, has a brownish coat in the summer which changes to white in the winter. Only the 6in. black-tipped ears and 4in. white tail remain unchanged all the year round. This jack rabbit, which weighs up to 10 lb, lives in the prairies of the northwest, but to the south lives the smaller black-tailed or jackass hare. The latter name is derived from the 8in. black-tipped ears. The coat is sandy except for the black upper surface of the tail. It does not turn white in winter. This species lives in the arid country from Oregon to Mexico and eastwards to Texas. There is also a small population in Florida which has come from imported jack rabbits, used in training greyhounds, that have gone wild.

The remaining jack rabbits, the two species of antelope or white-sided jack rabbits, live in restricted areas of Arizona and New Mexico.

Safety in bounding leaps

Like all hares, jack rabbits live on the surface of the ground and do not burrow. The exception is the white-tailed jack rabbit which in winter burrows under the snow for warmth and also gains protection against predators such as owls. Otherwise jack rabbits escape detection by crouching among the sparse vegetation of the prairies and semi-desert countryside. They lie up in shade during the day and come out in the evening. Each jack rabbit has several forms, hollows in the ground shaded and concealed by plants, within its home range. If flushed, jack rabbits will run extremely fast, sometimes reaching 45 mph in a series of 20ft springing bounds like animated rubber balls. Every so often they leap up 4 or 5 ft to clear the surrounding vegetation and look out for enemies.

Water from cacti

Jack rabbits feed mainly on grass and plants such as sagebrush or snakeweed, and often become serious pests where their numbers build up. To protect crops and to save the grazing for domestic stock, hunts are organised or poisoned bait put down. In the arid parts of their range, when the grass has dried up, jack rabbits survive on mes-

Hare of the plain and prairie: the jack rabbit of the western United States has two obvious adaptations for grassland life — very long ears, useful for detecting predators at a distance, and long hind legs with which it runs up to 45 mph in a series of bounding leaps.

quite and cacti. They can get all the water they need from cacti providing they do not lose too much moisture in keeping cool. To eat a prickly cactus a jack rabbit carefully chews around a spiny area and pulls out the loosened section. Then it puts its head into the hole and eats the moist, fleshy pulp which it finds inside.

Born in the open
The length of the breeding season varies according to the range of the jack rabbit, many as eight. The babies weigh 2–6 oz and can stand and walk a few steps immediately after birth, but they do not leave the nest for about 4 weeks.

Radiator ears

Large ears are a characteristic of desert animals, such as bat-eared and fennec foxes, and it is usually supposed that as well as improving the animal's hearing they act as radiators for keeping the body cool. as a means of cooling. In hot weather jack rabbits make use of every bit of shade and in their forms the ground temperature is lower than the air or body temperature and so acts as another heat sink.

The heat balance of a jack rabbit is, however, very precarious. On a hot day it is possible for two men easily to run down a jack rabbit. By continually flushing it and keeping it in the open the jack rabbit soon collapses from heat exhaustion and is soon ready for the pot!

Meston

L Lee Rue III: Photo Res

being shorter in the north. At the onset of breeding jack rabbits indulge in the typical mad antics of hares. The males chase to and fro and fight each other. They rear up, sometimes growling, and batter each other with their forepaws. They also bite each other, tearing out tufts of fur or even flesh and occasionally violent kicks are delivered with the hindlegs. A carefully-aimed kick can wound the recipient severely; otherwise the fight continues until one of the combatants turns tail and flees.

The baby jack rabbits are born in open nests concealed by brush or grass and lined with fur which the female pulls from her body. The litters are usually of three or four young but there may be as few as one or as

There is, however, a drawback to this idea. If heat can be lost from the ears it can also be absorbed. The problem has now been resolved because it has been realised that a clear sky has a low radiant temperature and acts as a heat sink. In the semi-arid home of the black-tailed jack rabbit a clear, blue sky may have a temperature of $10-15°C/50-59°F$ to which heat can be radiated from the jack rabbit's ears that have a temperature of $38°C/100°F$. Only a slight difference in temperature is needed for radiation to take place and the large difference between ears and sky allows efficient heat transfer.

Jack rabbits rely on radiation to keep them cool, for, as we have seen, they do not get enough water to be able to use evaporation

◁△ *On the look-out. White-tailed jack rabbit crouches by sparse vegetation of the prairies.*
△ *Black-tailed portrait. Named jackass hare, after its 8in. black-tipped ears, this jack rabbit does not change to white in winter as does the white-tailed jack rabbit.*

class	**Mammalia**
order	**Lagomorpha**
family	**Leporidae**
genus & species	***Lepus californicus** black-tailed jack rabbit* ***L. townsendi*** *white-tailed jack rabbit* *others*

Jaguar

*This is the largest of the American cats and is known as **el tigre** in South America. The jaguar is no longer than a leopard but is more heavily built; head and body are 5—6 ft long and the tail is about 3 ft. It may weigh up to 300 lb. The ground colour of the coat is yellow, becoming paler underneath. All over the body is a pattern of black spots up to 1 in. diameter. The jaguar's coat is usually easy to distinguish from the spotted coat of a leopard because the spots on the jaguar skin are arranged in a rosette of 4—5 around a central spot. These rosettes are not so marked on the legs or head where the spots are more tightly packed. Black and albino jaguars are known.*

Jaguars range from the southern United States to Patagonia. In places it is still quite common but elsewhere it has been shot as a cattle-stealer and for its beautiful coat and is now rare or missing altogether.

▷ *'Jaguara'—the South American Indian name for the jaguar—is said to mean the 'carnivore that overcomes its prey in a single bound'.*

Jaguar
(Panthera onca)

Zool Soc London

Little-known cat

Although they are found on the plains of Patagonia and the mountains of the Andes, the main home of jaguars is dense forests, especially near water. They come into open country when food is plentiful there. They are good climbers, rivalling the leopard in their ability to prowl through trees, often hunting their prey along branches. In some areas that are flooded for part of the year, jaguars are confined to trees—except when they take to water for they are extremely good swimmers as well. Jaguars are difficult to find in their forest haunts because their spotted coats blend in so well with their surroundings. As a result less is known about jaguars than about other big cats.

Our knowledge is based mainly on the stories of South American Indians and the accounts of explorers and hunters.

It is likely that jaguars have territories or ranges which they defend against other jaguars. This explains reports by travellers in the South American forests of being followed by a jaguar for many miles, then suddenly being abandoned. Apparently the jaguars had been seeing the men off their territories.

Man-killers

Jaguars take a wide variety of food. Their main prey is capybaras and peccaries and they also capture large animals such as tapirs and domestic cattle as well as sloths,

anteaters, monkeys and deer. They fight, kill and devour alligators and wait for freshwater turtles to come ashore to lay their eggs. The turtles are tipped onto their backs and the jaguars rip open their shells. Their eggs are also dug up.

Another favourite food is fish, which are caught by the jaguar lying in wait on a rock or a low branch overhanging the water and flipping the fish out with a quick strike of the paw. It is sometimes said that jaguars flip their tails in the water to act as a lure. Their tails may hang into the water and attract fish accidentally, and as cats often flick their tails when excited this could be especially attractive to fish. Having done this by chance and met with success it would

1149

not be beyond the mental powers of a jaguar to learn to do it deliberately.

Inevitably there should be stories of man-eating connected with the jaguar, as there are with any big carnivore. According to some accounts it is more dangerous than the lion or leopard, partly because of its habit of defending a territory and partly because it becomes possessive about its prey. When the prey is domestic stock men living and working nearby are likely to be attacked. In these cases, however, the jaguars are man-killing rather than man-eating. Another cause of attacks is the wounding of jaguars by hunters. Jaguars are hunted with dogs that bring them to bay after tiring them, and an enraged jaguar may charge, killing dogs or hunter. In exoneration of the jaguar, the famous explorer and naturalist Humboldt tells of two Indian children playing in a forest clearing. They were joined by a jaguar who bounded around them until it accidentally scratched the face of one child. The other seized a stick and smote the jaguar on the face; the wild beast slunk back into the jungle. How much truth lies in the story is impossible to say, but it is not the first account of a large beast playing with children.

Year-round breeding

Jaguars breed at any time of the year and have cubs every other year. Gestation lasts about 100 days and 2—4 cubs are born in each litter. Virtually nothing is known of courtship or care of the young in the wild because of the difficulty of making observations. Jaguars have lived in captivity for 22 years.

Peccary foes

It is thought jaguars 'take possession' of their prey and defend it. Indians in Guyana have told of jaguars attaching themselves to herds of peccaries and following them about, preying on those that get separated from their fellows. It is also said that the peccaries, which can be very savage, will attempt to rescue their companions and send the jaguar running to the nearest tree. This is supported by the account of an English explorer in Brazil who, hearing a great commotion one evening, found a jaguar perched on an anthill surrounded by about 50 furious peccaries. Inadvertently the jaguar lowered its tail which was immediately grabbed by the peccaries, who pulled the jaguar down and tore it apart. This may be a tall story—but at the moment much of our knowledge of jaguars has to rest on such stories.

class	**Mammalia**
order	**Carnivora**
family	**Felidae**
genus & species	***Panthera onca***

Prowling around—jaguar cubs. The spotted coat has groups of black rosettes similar to the leopard's, but in jaguars each rosette has a central spot.

Jaguarundi

Although a member of the cat family the jaguarundi is more like a large weasel in shape and habits. Its body is long, its legs very short and its head is flattened with small ears and sloping face. A jaguarundi, sometimes spelt jaguarondi, may be up to 50 in. head and body with a tail of 21 in. but its height at the shoulder will not exceed 12 in. Its weight may be up to 20 lb. Its short fur is uniformly rusty-red or grey, these being distinct colour phases of the same species, although at one time the red was believed to be a separate species with the common name of the eyra or eyra cat and a separate scientific name *Felis eyra*. Its name is derived from the name used for this animal by the Tupi, an aboriginal people in Brazil. Jaguarundis live in grasslands, on the edges of forests or in dense brushland, especially near water, from the southern border of the United States southwards to northern Argentina in South America.

Otter-like cat

Jaguarundis are extremely shy and secretive. They are seldom seen and from what little is known of their habits they are more like otters than cats. In some parts of America they are called otter-cats. Instead of stalking their prey or lying in wait they pursue it. Excellent runners despite their short legs, they will sprint for a mile or more if necessary, even through dense undergrowth, running down rodents and ground birds. They readily take to water, another un-catlike trait, and they can climb trees. They do this in search of fruit and have been seen feeding, in company with howler monkeys, on green figs. The gestation period is said to be 9 months, which is unusually long for a member of the cat family, but as jaguarundis are not easy to keep in captivity this figure is unverified.

Colour phases

The jaguarundi is a species showing colour phases. In all species there is a variation from one individual to another in the coat, the plumage and so on. Colour phases, how-ever, are rather special. In dealing with the blotched genet (p 859) we saw that a related form, the rusty-spotted genet, was believed to be a colour phase of it. There are several species of the cat family in which this is more definite. In the jaguarundi there may be red individuals or grey individuals. The African tiger-cat of the tropical rain forests may be red or grey and the colours are interchangeable. A red-coated individual may be grey after the next moult and vice versa. Temminck's cat, also known as the golden cat, of southeast Asia, may be uniformly red or uniformly grey, or it may be red with black spots or grey with black spots and a single litter may contain kittens showing two or more of these four colour phases. The colours are quite distinct and do not grade into each other.

The Jaguarundi has yet to be studied closely in the wild. In South America it frequents grasslands, edges of forests or dense brushland, especially near water. It is also known as the otter cat—not for any particular affinity it has for swimming—but for its long, low profile and otter size. To date specimens have not been kept in captivity with great success. The two captive youngsters on this page, however, seem to be pictures of health and liveliness.

class	**Mammalia**
order	**Carnivora**
family	**Felidae**
genus & species	*Felis yagouaroundi*

Jaguarundi
(Felis yagouaroundi)

Java sparrow

Java sparrows are known the world over as popular cage birds which breed well in the right conditions. There are several varieties, including pied, cinnamon and white. The natural plumage is bluish-grey with a pink belly and black rump and tail. The head is black with large white ear patches and the bill is pinkish white. The total length is 5 in., 1 in. less than a house sparrow.

The original home of the Java sparrow was on the islands of Java and Bali but it has been introduced to many parts of southeast Asia. It is also called the Java finch, ricebird and Java temple bird.

Rice-eating sparrows

Java sparrows are such a pest in southeast Asia, where rice is the main crop, that even their scientific name *Padda oryzivora* means 'paddy field rice-eater'. In captivity they feed on paddy rice alone largely ignoring other food unless the rice is not available. They may also take other seeds such as canary and millet and green food as substitutes and they eat mealworms, and termites. This variation in diet seems to depend on the conditions they are kept in and whether they are breeding.

Old World courtesy

Pairs of Java sparrows live amicably together, sharing the same roost and greeting each other on meeting. If the pair has been separated and then allowed to meet again they perform an elaborate and charming ceremony. The first stage is a low bow, trilling at the same time. Then they perch side by side and each in turn twists sidewards and rests its head over that of its mate. This is followed by more bowing and the birds continue sitting very close to each other for some time.

The male Java sparrow's song is a fluting, sometimes whistling, note which varies between individuals. Writers have given quite different descriptions of the song, which can be heard when the female is out of sight of the male as well as during courtship. At the start of the courtship display the male bows in a 'hunched' posture, different from the meeting bow, and jumps up and down on the perch, waving his bill from side to side and twisting his tail towards the waiting female. As he nears her he begins to sing. Sometimes the female bows and bounces as well, the pair of them making a very pretty sight, before crouching with tail quivering. If the female rejects the male's advances she may put her head over his as in the meeting ceremony or even attack him, pecking at his bill.

Female finishes the nest

The nest is built from grasses and other plant materials, that are long, flexible and tough. They are woven into a loose ball and the chamber so formed is lined with feathers. In captivity the male has been seen to do all the nest building. The female accompanies her mate on his trips for collecting material but helps him only at the end when she collects feathers for the lining.

Both sexes incubate the eggs, taking turns of 20–30 minutes. The chicks hatch after

*'Paddyfield rice-eater' — scientific name **Padda oryzivora** means this. It results from the raids the Java sparrows make on the rice fields of southeast Asia.*

about 3 weeks' incubation. They are completely naked at first and are brooded and fed by both parents.

Feather beds

In the *Avicultural Magazine* Derek Goodwin has recounted how his pet Java sparrows took to roosting with turtle doves. Each evening they would nestle against the much larger turtle doves and if possible climb between their legs. When the turtle doves nested the Java sparrows climbed under the incubating bird. This behaviour has been reported by other cage bird fanciers. Sometimes the Java sparrows roosted on top of the doves instead of underneath them. Why they should do this is a mystery. They do not clump like avadavats (p 100), except with their mates, so the doves are not being used as imitation gatherings of Java sparrows. Neither are they nestling against the doves to keep warm—this behaviour has been seen in temperatures of 32°C/90°F in the shade. It would be very interesting to know if wild Java sparrows make use of a wild species of dove in this same way.

class	**Aves**
order	**Passeriformes**
family	**Estrildidae**
genus & species	***Padda oryzivora***

André Fatras

Constance P Warner

◁ *The beautiful blue jay of North America.
This bird has an unmistakable black collar
around its neck and blue plumage on the back.*
◁▽ *Mouths forever open—the common jay
has a full-time job keeping the fledglings happy.*
▷ *Cayenne jay lives in South American forests.*

Jay

*Unlike most other members of the crow
family jays are highly colourful. They
make up a very varied subfamily of over
40 species, 32 of which are in America
and all but four of these are South
American. The most widely ranging is the
common jay of Europe and Asia, which is
selected here to represent the subfamily.*

*The common jay, 13½ in. long, has a
reddish brown plumage, darker on the
back and wings than on the breast. It
has a white head streaked with black and
the feathers are raised in a crest in
moments of excitement. There is a conspicuous black moustache running from
the corner of the bill. The most noticeable
feature is the patch of blue feathers barred
with black on each wing. Jays are very
shy and the usual view of them is a black
tail and white rump in full retreat.*

*The next most common jay is the beauti-
ful blue jay of North America. Its plumage
is blue on the back, white on the front,*

*with black bars on wings and tail and a
black collar. The turquoise jay of the
Andes is blue all over, with conspicuous
black markings on the head running down
to the chest and outlining a gorget of
slightly lighter blue. The Siberian jay is
brown and grey, reddish on the wings,
rump and sides of the tail. The Canada
or grey jay is similar but lacks the red.
It has a white forehead and black nape.*

*Jays are considered to be more primitive
than other members of the crow family.
The pattern of their distribution suggests
a former wide distribution that is now
breaking up. For example, the North
American scrub jay is found on the
western side of the Rockies but there is a
small population in distant Florida.*

Shy but garrulous

The common jay lives in woods and forests
but comes out onto the open scrubland
around to feed. Highly secretive and shy,
its harsh cries can be heard among trees
for long periods without the bird showing
itself. Its flight is heavy and appears to be

laboured. The raucous cries and cat-like
mewing are the best known of its calls, but
it uses a very soft and melodious song in
spring. Jays are also good mimics and a
tame jay can mimic a wide range of mech-
anical sounds, bird song and human speech.
Even wild jays use vocal mimicry. For
instance one always hooted like a tawny owl
when it flew past the tree in which an owl
was known to roost.

Caches of buried food

The jay's diet is very varied and includes
seeds, fruits and small invertebrates such
as insects, spiders, earthworms, snails and
slugs. Soft fruits as well as apple, cherry
and plum are eaten. They also take eggs
and nestlings of small songbirds, wood
pigeons, mallard and pheasant. In autumn
the main food is acorns and large quantities
are eaten. A young jay, hand-reared and
isolated from its own kind will strip an acorn
of its husk in a way that suggests it knows
instinctively how to deal with it. Jays also
bury acorns, pecking a hole in the ground,
placing the acorn in it and then covering
it up. Tests have shown that, surprisingly,
jays can find these acorns again. They seem

▽ *The shy bird with the comical moustache. Common European jay anting. This behaviour is frequent among the crow family and song-birds. They take an ant in the bill and rub it on the wing feathers; but jays often go through the same motions without an ant in the bill.*

to remember where each acorn is buried and will return unerringly to it even when the spot is covered with leaf litter or snow.

Courtship gatherings?

In spring jays indulge in what are called 'ceremonial assemblies' the significance of which is not yet clear. A dozen or more chase each other from tree to tree or among the branches of the trees uttering a chorus of soft warbling notes, delightful to the ear and in strong contrast with their usual harsh notes. It has been suggested that these assemblies may have something to do with the birds pairing off but this has not been confirmed. The breeding season is April—May, when a nest is built 5—20 ft from the ground in a tree. It is made of sticks with a little earth and lined with fine roots. In this 5—7 eggs are laid, green to buff coloured with fine dark mottlings, and scrawled with fine hairlines. Probably both parents incubate for 16 days and the young are fed for 3 weeks after hatching. It has yet to be proven that the two parents share the incubation. Male and female look alike and can only be distinguished by their behaviour when courting and mating.

Sharp eyesight

Experiments with a tame jay have shed light on the use of its eyes including the keenness of its sight. When linked with what is also known about jays' ability to find each acorn it has buried we get a striking picture of the extent to which birds depend on their eyesight. The owner of the tame jay in question noticed that when he went close to the bird's aviary and stood so that his own nose was only a few inches from the bird's beak the pupils of the jay's eyes were brought forward so that the bird was looking down its beak with both eyes. Whether this gives the jay stereoscopic vision is not known, but subsequent observation showed that many birds use their eyes in this way, when taking a close look at an object.

It was while he was looking at his jay in this manner that the owner saw the bird catch an insect. The jay, apparently looking its owner 'straight in the eye', suddenly flew to another perch in the aviary, 6 ft away and somewhat to the rear, pecked at the perch and flew back with a tiny insect in the tip of its beak. The insect was so small that the human eye would have difficulty in

picking it out at a range of 6 ft. Yet the jay, with its pupils directed forwards, had detected a slight movement, to the side and to the rear, had flicked one eye round and immediately flown over to take its prey.

class	**Aves**
order	**Passeriformes**
family	**Corvidae**
subfamily	**Garrulinae**
genera & species	***Aphelocoma coerulescens*** *North American scrub jay* ***Cyanocitta cristata*** *blue jay* ***Cyanolyca turcosa*** *turquoise jay* ***Cyanocorax cayanus*** *cayenne jay* ***Garrulus glandarius*** *common jay* ***Perisoreus canadensis*** *Canada or grey jay* ***P. infaustus*** *Siberian jay* *others*

Jellyfish

Jellyfish are free-swimming relatives of sea anemones, corals and hydroids, all belonging to the phylum Coelenterata. In the life cycles of many coelenterates there are two distinct phases. One is a free-living jellyfish, or medusa, that reproduces sexually, while the other develops from an embryo and is an anchored, or sessile, polyp, or colony of polyps, that in turn buds off jellyfish. One or other phase may be dominant and the other less important or even non-existent. The large jellyfishes make up one class, the Scyphozoa (or Scyphomedusae), in which the polyp stage is very small. Attention will be concentrated here on this group.

Upside-down hydra

The typical jellyfish is umbrella-shaped, globular or conical with 4 or 8 tentacles around the margin, or many tentacles may form a ring around the margin. Under the umbrella, and like a handle to it, is the mouth, leading into the digestive cavity. The mouth is drawn out at the corners into four long lips. The basic form of the body can best be understood by comparison with that of hydra (p 1148). The body of hydra, as we have seen, consists essentially of two layers of cells forming a sac and separated by a very thin layer of non-cellular material, mesogloea. In the jellyfish the mesogloea is very thick. Although the body of a jellyfish is more elaborate than that of hydra it still has the same two-layered structure and ring of tentacles around the mouth.

Some common jellyfish

A jellyfish found in seas throughout the world and which is common off the coasts of Europe is *Aurelia aurita*. It grows to nearly 1½ ft across, with many very short tentacles. The blue, yellowish, reddish or brown jellyfish *Cyanea*, also known as sea blubber, can reach 6 ft across in Arctic waters but is usually less than half that. The jellyfish *Chrysaora* has 24 tentacles, and these may be 20 yd long in one species. Around the centre of its white or yellowish disc there is often a brownish ring from which streaks of the same colour radiate. Another common jellyfish is *Rhizostoma*, or 'the root-mouthed', named for the shape of its lips. It is a whitish dome, about a foot across, with a deep purple rim. It has no tentacles but is easily recognized by the cauliflower-like oral lips. In the United States it is called

'cabbage blebs'. Some jellyfish are luminescent and one of the most intense, which is occasionally found in north European waters, is *Pelagia noctiluca*.

Different ways of feeding

Jellyfish swim by rhythmic pulsations of the umbrella or bell. The movement is very like an umbrella being opened and shut slowly. It is co-ordinated by a very simple nervous system and by sense organs around the edge that are sensitive to light, gravity and chemicals in the water. Jellyfish are carnivorous and many of them capture fish, shrimps and other animals on their trailing tentacles, paralyse them with their stinging cells and transfer them to the mouth. *Aurelia* catches fish when young, but once grown to about 1 in. across feeds in quite a different way on small planktonic animals. These are trapped in sticky mucus all over the surface of the body and are driven by cilia to the rim. There the accumulating blobs are licked off by the 4 long oral lips. Further cilia propel the food in currents of water into the digestive cavity, from which a system of branching, cilia-lined canals radiate out to the rim, carrying food to all parts of the body. *Rhizostoma* feeds in the manner of a sponge, drawing in small planktonic animals by means of ciliary currents through thousands of separate mouths on the greatly elaborated oral lips. It is these mouths and the many little sensory palps on the oral lips that give the jellyfish its characteristic cauliflower appearance. Another plankton feeder is a tropical jellyfish *Cassiopeia* which lies mouth upwards on the sea bottom in shallow water, pulsating its bell gently and capturing plankton with its lips as it is wafted by. It has symbiotic algae in its oral lips which benefit from the sunlight falling on them (see also anemone *Anthopleura*, p 45, and clam, p 450).

Piles of saucers

The common *Aurelia* is readily recognised by the four nearly oval purple or lilac reproductive organs, ovaries in the females, testes in the males. These lie in pouches in the digestive cavity but show through the transparent bell. The male sheds his sperm into the sea and these are wafted to the female and taken in along with her food. The eggs are fertilised and develop for a while in pouches on the oral lips. They are eventually set free as tiny planula larvae which soon attach themselves to seaweed or stone and develop into small polyps, known as scyphistomas or hydratubas, each with 16 tentacles. From the base of each, stolons,

like runners of strawberry plants, grow out and new polyps develop on them. Each polyp eventually gives rise in the following winter to a number of young jellyfish called ephyra larvae, not round like the adult, but with the edge of the bell drawn out into 8 arms, notched at the tips. To do this, the polyp becomes pinched off into segments so it resembles a pile of lobed saucers. Then the tissue connecting these saucers contracts and snaps and each one swims off as a little ephyra. The growing ephyras transform gradually into adults by filling in the spaces between the arms.

An alternation of forms like this is typical of these jellyfish, though, in *Pelagia*, the egg develops directly into an ephyra.

Sea wasps

Jellyfishes are practically all water. A jellyfish stranded on the shore will soon vanish under the hot rays of the sun leaving little more than a patch of water in the sand. Their bodies are nearly 99% jelly and the whole body contains less than 5% organic matter. Yet jellyfishes can be extremely venomous as anyone knows who has hauled on a rope covered in long trailing tentacles. The stings of jellyfishes come from the many stinging cells or nematocysts which shoot out a poisonous thread when touched. The severity of the sting depends very much on the number of nematocysts discharged and also on the type of jellyfish. The most venomous jellyfishes are those living in the coral seas and the least troublesome are those in temperate seas, but even these, if enough tentacles are allowed to touch our bodies, can sometimes lead to a loss of consciousness and, in the case of one bather to drowning. This kind of accident is happily very rare. The most venomous jellyfishes belong to what are known as the Cubomedusae, so called because of their somewhat squarish shape. They range in size from as small as grapes to as large as pears and have four tentacles or four groups of tentacles. Some of these, like bathers, seem to prefer quiet shallow waters in the warmer seas, and are particularly troublesome around the northern Australian coasts, the Philippines and Japan. They have been called sea wasps and they can kill in as short a time as half a minute, usually in a quarter of an hour, the victim dying in excruciating pain.

phylum	**Coelenterata**
class	**Scyphozoa**

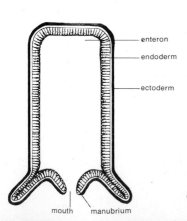

mouth   manubrium

Diagram to show the relation between the sedentary polyp (left) and the freely drifting medusa (right). The intermediate form (centre) is an imaginary stage showing the transition from polyp to medusa. The common jellyfish is a medusa stage.

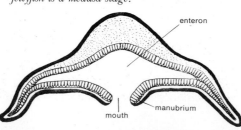

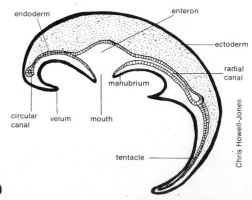

Chris Howell-Jones

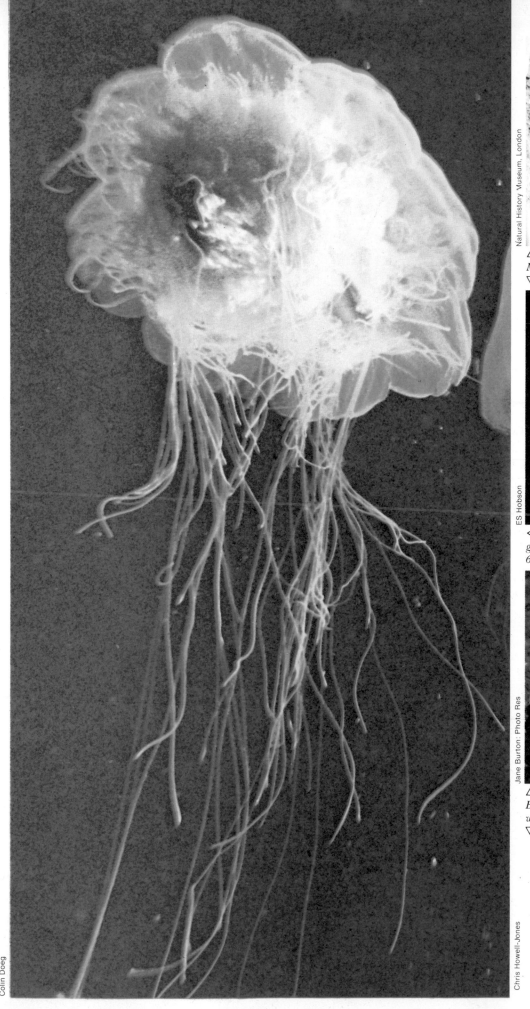

△ *Plaster cast of a 600 million year old* **Mawsonites spriggi**, *a jellyfish-like animal.*
▽ *Beautifully luminescent—* **Pelagia colorata**.

◁ *Young* **Cyanea** *or sea blubber. This is the giant among jellyfish sometimes growing up to 6 ft with trailing tentacles 200 ft long.*

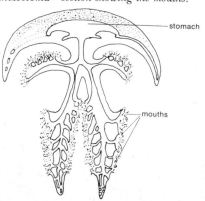

△ **Cassiopeia**—*a tropical rhizostome medusa. Beneath the flat top protrude the white arms with thousands and thousands of grey mouths.*
▽ **Rhizostoma**—*section showing the mouths.*

stomach

mouths

Drifting splendour, great . . .

This association between **Aurelia** *and* **Pugettia**, *a spider crab, has only been seen in the last decade. The habits of these two animals are so different, the jellyfish is planktonic, the crab benthonic (bottom living) that the association is thought to be of chance contact and not where one animal is dependent on the other. Crabs have been seen clinging to medusae, penetrating into the mesogloea and feeding on medusan tissue without any apparent lasting harm to crabs or jellyfish*

Chrysaora isosceles. *This jellyfish is like* **Aurelia** *in shape and general plan except it has 24 long trailing tentacles around its margin which are used to capture food and the lips are extended into four frilly 'oral arms'.*

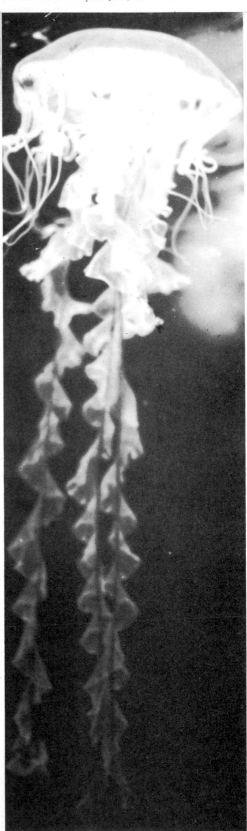

JM Clayton: NHPA

HH Stellrecht

. . . and small

The polyp generation of **Aurelia aurita**, like all other jellyfish, is a small sedentary phase passing the winter hanging from a rock. In spring the polyp becomes divided by transverse grooves, a process known as strobilisation, until it looks like a pile of saucers. Each 'saucer' is called an ephyra, a young medusa which eventually breaks off from the top of segmented polyp or scyphistoma and swims away, growing finally into a large free-floating adult jellyfish.

The free ephyra (top) a few mm in diameter is beautifully symmetrical and looks very graceful in profile (centre). Equally awe-inspiring is the bell of this moon jelly, the adult version of **Aurelia aurita** (bottom).

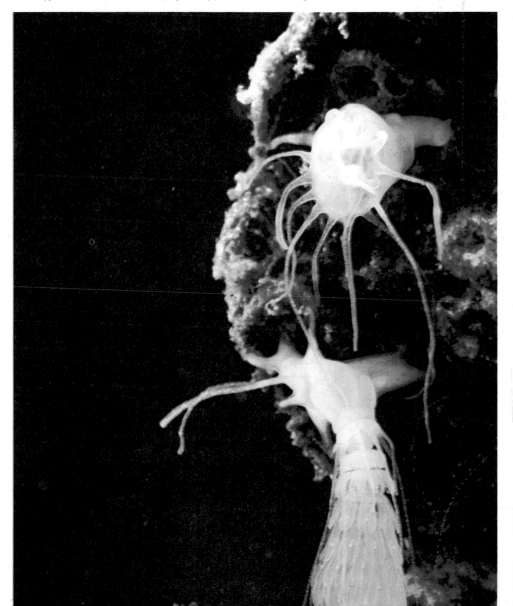

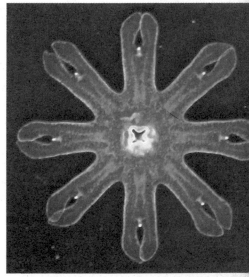

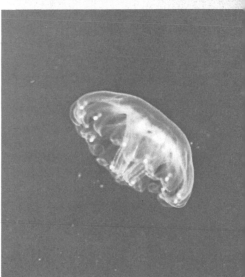

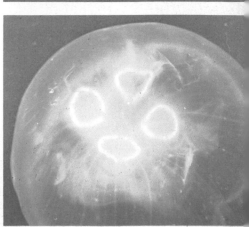

Jerboa

Jerboas are small desert-living rodents, the 'desert rats' of the Second World War. They look rather like kangaroos, having long hindlegs, very short forelegs and long tails. Like kangaroos they travel by hopping. Other desert-living rodents have developed hopping as a means of travelling across sparsely covered ground but in none are there such great differences between fore and hindlegs as there are in the jerboas, where hindlegs are four times longer than the forelegs.

The head and body lengths of jerboas range from 1½ to 6 in., the hindlegs from 1 to 3 in. The tail is longer than the head and body, ranging from 3 to 10 in. and often bears a white tuft at the tip. It is used as a balancer when hopping and as a prop when the jerboa is sitting upright. The fur is fine and usually sandy coloured, matching the ground where jerboas live. Some species have long rabbit-like ears and others have short mouse-like ears. Jerboas are found in northern Africa and Asia east to northern China and Manchuria.

Avoiding the heat
Jerboas survive the desert heat by living in burrows and coming out in the cool of night to forage among the sparse vegetation. Their burrows are usually found near vegetation, especially along the edges of fields, but in the rainy season they make burrows in mounds or in the sides of hills where they will escape flooding. At this time of year the entrances to the burrows are left open but during the hot summer occupied holes have plugs of soil blocking the entrances. The plugs keep out hot air, and, probably, predators. Jerboas' burrows often have an emergency exit that ends just below the surface or opens at the surface but is filled with loose earth. When disturbed the jerboa bursts through this exit and escapes. The Asiatic jerboas dig winter burrows, 10 ft or more long, which may be plugged, and are consequently very difficult to trace. Except when a female has a family, usually one jerboa lives in each burrow.

The burrows are dug very rapidly, the jerboas scraping at the sandy soil with their sharp-clawed forefeet and pushing it back with the hindfeet. Even the nose is used, for pushing earth back or tamping the walls of the burrow. Some species have a fold of skin on the nose that can be drawn over the nostrils to keep sand out.

When chased, jerboas can move very fast, covering up to 10 ft at each bound and reaching speeds of up to 15 mph. Otherwise they 'trot', jumping 4—5 in. at each bound and often stopping. The only time they walk on all fours is when feeding. It is a very awkward movement with nose down, rump in the air and tail dragging on the ground.

Feeding on succulents
Jerboas feed on desert plants, both succulent and dry. During the rainy season there is plenty of fresh, sprouting greenery. As the plants dry up the jerboas dig out roots in which water is stored, but in the dry season they survive on dry seeds. In some places jerboas attack crops of water melons and rubber, and certain species feed on beetles and other insects. The jaws of jerboas are weaker than those of gerbils so they cannot eat hard seeds.

The jerboas' bounding gait allows them to cover a large area in search of food with the minimum loss of energy. This is vital in the dry season when food is scarce. Unlike gerbils (p 862) jerboas do not store food.

Slow-growing babies
Jerboas are mainly solitary animals; each jerboa has its own burrow and forages by itself, although sometimes loose colonies are formed. Some species appear to have communal burrows but the function of these is not known.

Breeding probably takes place twice a year in most species and some may have more than two litters, but the young of the last litter may die before reaching maturity if they are born too near the start of the dry season. Litters are of 2—6, usually 3 babies. Very little is known about the jerboas' breeding habits, partly because the animals are nocturnal and elusive and partly because they have failed to breed in captivity. Pregnant females have been captured and have given birth to their young, but all too often they have then ignored them. The few families that have been raised show that jerboas develop more slowly than laboratory rats. They are born naked and crawl with their forelegs, the hindlegs not developing until they are 8 weeks old, and they cannot jump until 11 weeks old. They are weaned at 8 weeks and are sexually mature at 14 weeks, twice the age at which rats mature. Jerboas, however, live longer: 6 years compared with the rat's 3 years.

Escape by speed
Unlike other rodents jerboas do not dash for their burrows or other cover when pursued but make their escape by bounding away at high speed with frequent changes of direction and occasionally leaping vertically. They have many enemies and are probably eaten by every predator that comes across them, especially foxes, fennecs, owls and perhaps snakes. Bedouin Arabs catch them by flooding or digging out their burrows and by setting traps.

A dry diet

By living in a cool, humid burrow and emerging at night jerboas can escape the worst of the desert heat, but conditions are still severe by comparison with those in temperate climates and like other desert animals jerboas face the problem of water shortage. They economise on water by living in burrows and, in the hottest weather, becoming dormant. So efficient are they at conserving the water in their bodies that they can survive the summer on dry seeds containing very little moisture, while in the laboratory jerboas have lived for 3 years on a diet of dry seeds. By comparison, rats could survive for only a few days. The jerboas' survival on this diet is due to their ability to hold water in their body and pass a very concentrated, acidic urine, although in these circumstances jerboas are much less active so less body waste is formed and water can be conserved.

class	**Mammalia**
order	**Rodentia**
family	**Dipodidae**
genera & species	***Allactaga sibirica*** ***Dipus sagitta*** *feather-footed jerboa* ***Jaculus jaculus*** *desert jerboa* *others*

Nose to the ground, hindlegs splayed and tail trailing — the desert jerboa forages for food.

Jewel fish

This is one of the most beautiful of African cichlids and a favourite with aquarists as well as with those studying fish behaviour. The adults are gorgeously coloured and seem to be spangled with jewels. They are up to 4 in. long and the colouration is similar in both male and female although at times the female is the more brilliant. The male has, however, more 'jewels' especially on the gill-covers and a more pronounced crescent on the tail fin. The general colouring is dark olive to grey brown with a greenish sheen and there are 6–7 rows of sky-blue spots along each side of the body.

Little savages

The colours of the beautifully patterned jewel fish play an important part in its life. They help it find a mate and protect it as a baby. As the time for egg laying approaches the red on the body becomes more intense and covers a larger part of the body. Male and female spend much time lying side by side on the sandy bottom during a period of 2–3 days then they begin to clean a hard surface for the eggs. These, $\frac{1}{20}$ in. long, are laid in rows, looking like small strings of tiny pearls, the male following to fertilise each row, until a rounded patch of eggs covers the surface, 500–700 in all. The female fans the eggs with her pectoral fins to aerate them, the male taking over when she leaves to feed. When the baby fishes are about 7 days old they begin to feed, first on

babies will soon be eaten, so the parents must have some way of calling their broods to them when danger threatens, and the babies must have some way of recognizing when their parents are calling them.

In some of the earliest of the experiments three glass aquaria were placed side by side with their long sides touching. Some baby jewel fish were put in the middle tank and in each of the end tanks was put a disc on a long rod, the rods being fixed above on a converted windscreen wiper. When this was set going the disc in each of the end aquaria moved back and forth in sight of the baby fishes. One disc was painted scarlet, the other was painted black. As soon as the discs started moving the young jewel fish moved over to the side of their aquarium nearest the scarlet disc.

Barry Pengilley

This jewel-spangled African cichlid is a favourite among aquarists. Although it is only 4 in. long when fully grown it will bully other fishes in a tank and so for this reason is best kept in a separate aquarium. Even so a group of jewel fish makes a beautiful display.

There are also 3 larger dark spots on each side, one on the gill-cover, one in the centre of the flank and one at the base of the tail fin. These are more pronounced in the male than the female. There are scarlet edges to the fins, and the body more especially of the female is tinged with red or scarlet over the head, shoulders and belly. These remarks on colour can only be general because there is so much change, with the breeding season and with the mood of the fish, and it can happen sometimes that the male is the brighter of the two.

The jewel fish is found in rivers over most of tropical Africa, from the Niger and Congo to the Nile.

protistans, then on rotifers and small crustaceans. After a month they look like the parents and although small they start to fight, their pugnacious character coming out at an early age. They grow $\frac{3}{4}$ in. a month.

A colour-key for mothers

The behaviour of the jewel fish is very like that of the Jack Dempsey, which has also been much studied in aquaria. Attention will be given therefore to other features of the behaviour, notably to the part colour plays in keeping the baby fishes with their parents. It will be of interest to describe how the experiments are carried out.

The parent jewel fishes, like the parent Jack Dempseys, herd their brood when they are able to swim. This is a necessary protection because if left on their own the·

When young fishes leave home

Having done this the experimenters then used different sizes of discs, 1–3 in. diameter. They also used different coloured discs and they tried the effect of having the discs merely hanging in the end tanks or having them move quickly or slowly. They also experimented with broods of different ages. This meant hundreds of tests and the results show the following. Baby jewel fishes are born with a preference for scarlet over all other colours. Some colours, such as yellow or dark blue, did not attract them in the slightest. Their preference for scarlet becomes even stronger as they get older, so besides having the built-in preference for the main colour on the mother's body, this grows stronger as the young fish grows in size. There comes a time, however,

when the baby fish's liking for red declines. This is when it is several weeks old, and when it is time for the young fish to leave its parents' care. The waning effect of red makes it stray farther from its parents. As this is happening to all members of the brood the family eventually breaks up.

Size is important

The results of the experiments also show that size is important. A baby jewel fish will swim over to any disc coloured red but will swim over more slowly to one that is only 1 in. diameter than it will to one that is 2 or 3 in. diameter. Parent jewel fishes are about 2−3 in. long. Movement also makes a difference. A scarlet disc that is not moving will not attract the baby jewel fishes, or will not attract them strongly. In the same way a sluggish parent will not be able to call its brood together effectively. An active parent, sensing danger, moves more quickly and so imparts a sense of urgency to its brood. Moreover, at such times, the mother jewel fish raises and lowers her unpaired fins several times in succession and this fin flicking acts as a signal to bring her babies rapidly towards the red on her body.

In other species of cichlids which herd their broods as the jewel fish do the same results have been obtained except that the babies respond most to discs coloured like their parents, to black discs if the parents have black blotches or large black spots, and so on. Similar tests made on courting fishes show similar results. For example, a jewel fish is more attracted to a partner which not only shows red but moves quickly than to one that shows even more red but moves sluggishly. It is an advantage for a female jewel fish to choose a mate that moves quickly. He will be much more likely to protect her eggs after they are laid.

△ *The eggs are laid in rows on a clean rock. Once fertilised both parents take it in turns to fan the eggs with their pectoral fins.*

▽ *An attentive parent spits tiny straying baby jewel fish back onto the nursery stone. If allowed to stray they would soon be eaten.*

No two alike

The detailed colour pattern of the jewel fish has its value as well as the general colour. Once two· fishes have paired they recognize each other even when among a crowd of their own kind which to our eyes all look alike. A male jewel fish will know his own mate when there are several females in his territory. He will drive the others away but will not molest her, and tests have shown that he recognizes her by small differences in the pattern of her colours. When the male of a pair is taken out of an aquarium and one or more strange males put in the female will attack these and try to drive them out but will welcome her mate when he is put back into the aquarium. There have been instances in which a female fish, after mating with a male, sees him the following year in a nearby aquarium and tries to get to him although another male has been put into her aquarium. So while the jewels of ornate fishes may be a joy to the human eye they play an important part in the life of a fish.

class	**Pisces**
order	**Perciformes**
family	**Cichlidae**
genus & species	*Hemichromis bimaculatus*

John Dory

This fish, of curious shape and habits, is included in an order known formerly as the Zeomorphi but now called Zeiformes. The non-classical scholar may be forgiven for translating these two names as god-like or god-shaped.

The John Dory has a very high and narrow body, flattened from side to side and rounded in outline, it is shaped like a plate. The large head has a mournful expression due to the drooping mouth and the jawbones are such that the mouth can be shot forward when seizing prey. The dorsal fin is in two parts, the front portion being high with the spines strong and, in older individuals, long and carried backwards to end in a line with the tail. The rear part of the dorsal fin and the anal fin that lies opposite it are soft and flexible. Along the bases of the dorsal and anal fins are spines, but the scales on the body are small and spineless, and the skin is smooth. There are also 8 — 9 spiny plates along the belly. The John Dory is grey to fawn or golden yellow with long blotches of reddish-purple, and on each flank just behind the gill covers is a large black spot with a yellow margin. The maximum length is 22½ in. and it can weigh up to 18 lb.

It lives in the Mediterranean and eastern Atlantic as far north as the southern and southwestern waters of the British Isles and only occasionally wanders as far north as Norway.

Cat-like stalking

The John Dory with its high plate-like body cannot chase its prey. Instead, it stalks its food, keeping its body rigid, swimming by waving its second dorsal and its anal fin, using the tail fin as a rudder. Its plate-like shape means it can slip easily through the water for short distances. Keeping its eyes on its prey, it gradually draws nearer and nearer to it, finally seizing it by shooting out its protrusible toothless mouth. While stalking it shows signs of excitement. It holds its dorsal fin erect and quivers its fins, its colours blushing and fading all the time. These signs of supposed excitement may have an added value. Seen from head-on the high and very narrow body looks like a thin vertical stripe. The colours coming and going and the quivering of the fins tend to blur even this, so the small fish being stalked is oblivious of impending danger and makes absolutely no attempt to swim away.

The John Dory lives at depths down to 300 ft and little is known about its way of life apart from what has been seen of occasional individuals kept in aquaria. It feeds almost exclusively on small fishes, especially young herring, pilchard and sand eels, although it has been seen to take shrimps in captivity. It takes only live food; a John Dory in an aquarium was seen to spit out a dead fish it had seized. Nevertheless, Dr Douglas Wilson at the Plymouth Aquarium was able, in due course, to persuade a captive John Dory to take strips of squid which looked like fish when dropped into water and slowly floated down.

Sexing the John Dory

There is no outward difference between the sexes. Only by dissection and by examining the roes is it possible to distinguish female from male. In the same way we learn that the eggs are $\frac{1}{16}$ in. diameter. It is likely that they are laid on sand, like the eggs of sand eels, in June to August.

Dual personality

The John Dory is used as a food-fish but people are divided on the quality of its flesh. There is also a division of opinion so far as its name is concerned. It seems to have a romantic ring, almost reminding one of the tang of the sea, so one suspects the fish might have been named after some swash-buckling buccaneer or other adventurous seadog. Then there is the story that the black marks on its flank are where the finger and thumb of St Peter pressed when he took the coin from the fish's mouth, so getting the name *Peterfisch* in Germany. But there is the same legend about the haddock, and also about a species of *Tilapia*, but since the John Dory and the haddock are both marine, the *Tilapia*, being a freshwater fish, should take the credit.

Two other suggestions rob it of any glamour it might have. One is that its name is a corruption of the Italian word *janitore*, for a doorkeeper, the other that it is from the French *jaune dorée*, because of its golden yellow colour. The scientific name is *Zeus faber*, the first name being that of the overlord of the Greek gods; the second is Latin for a blacksmith.

Kendall McDonald

J Vasserot: Jacana

class	**Pisces**
order	**Zeiformes**
family	**Zeidae**
genus & species	***Zeus faber***

△ *Never seeing the bright side of life the John Dory swims around with a permanent gloomy expression on its face. Apart from the unfortunate pout this fish has exquisite dorsal fin spines which grow trailing filaments and the large black flank spots. The legend goes that St Peter made these marks with his finger and thumb.*
◁ *Because of its high plate-like body the John Dory cannot chase its prey. Instead it stalks its food and seizes it by rapidly shooting out its toothless mouth.*
▽ *Head of John Dory with the mouth retracted (left) and protruded (right).*

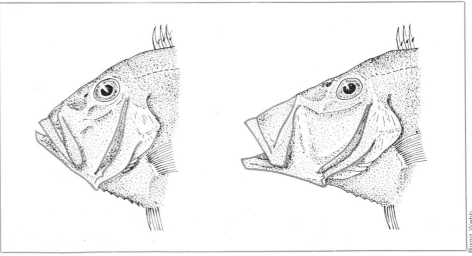

Birgit Webb

The stately male red jungle fowl takes a rest. This is the best known of the four species of jungle fowl. It has magnificent red plumage with an iridescent sheen. The cock has fleshy appendages, comb and lappets on his head, which mark them off from most of the pheasant family.

Jungle fowl

The four species of jungle fowl are not very closely related to the rest of the pheasant family. The cocks have the characteristic-fleshy appendages on their heads: a comb rises from the top of the head and lappets hang under the chin, while most of the face is naked. In the females the appendages are vestigial and the plumage is duller. The best known is the red jungle fowl from which the domestic chicken was derived. The plumage is mainly red and black with an iridescent greenish sheen. The red jungle fowl is found in the warmer parts of Asia from the Indian sub-continent to southern China and the Indonesian islands, but it is absent from

Borneo. The populations on various Pacific Islands such as the Philippines were probably introduced by man. The red jungle fowl has also been established in Natal, South Africa, and there are free-living populations in several parts of the world, for jungle fowl are popular with bird fanciers. The grey jungle fowl lives in the southern and western parts of the Indian peninsula, the green jungle fowl in Java and the fourth species is confined to Ceylon. The comb of the cock Ceylon jungle fowl is yellow with a red border. Its plumage is red and brown with greenish-black iridescent wings and tail and a purple rump.

In Australia some of the megapodes or brush-turkeys are known as jungle fowl.

Keeping out of the way

Jungle fowl live in forests and so their range is shrinking as forests are cut down and the country opened up for agriculture. They probably survive because they are extremely wary. Jungle fowl come out into clearings, roadsides and fields to feed, especially in early morning or after rain, but run for cover at the first alarm.

Even when undisturbed they are still wary. Some jungle fowl have been watched in the bamboo jungle of Thailand. They live in small flocks of one cock with 2–5 hens. In the morning the flock leave their roosts 15–20 ft up in the bamboos and are led down by the cock to drink at a stream. While the hens are drinking the cock keeps watch from a nearby perch. When the hens have finished the cock drinks hurriedly, then quickly leads his flock back to cover.

Scratching for food

The food of jungle fowl consists of virtually anything they can find in the leaf litter and soil of the forest floor, including green plants, seeds, berries, earthworms, insects and other small animals. They feed like domestic chickens, scratching violently with their strong toes and stepping back to search for anything brought to light.

In Ceylon the nellu plants form a great part of the undergrowth in the forests. They flower at intervals of several years and large numbers of jungle fowl and other birds gather to feast on the seeds.

Fighting cocks

Jungle fowl breed during most of the year but more often during the rainy season. The cocks are more aggressive than most of the

by scraping a hollow in the ground but sometimes uses the top of a tree stump or takes over the abandoned nest of a large bird. The eggs, usually 2—4, are speckled and are incubated for 19—21 days. The chicks can walk and feed themselves almost as soon as they are hatched. They can fly when a week old, when they begin to roost in the trees.

Safe perch

Jungle fowl fall prey to all manner of flesh-eating animals. Their only defence is to be extremely wary and to take flight at the first alarm. The exception is the incubating hen who will not leave the nest until the last moment. The roosts where the jungle fowl spend the night are chosen with care. Foliage shelters the sleeping jungle fowl

every 100 chicks survived their first year of life. Threequarters of the chicks never survived to independence and jungle fowl that did survive to maturity never lived more than 3 years.

There were probably very few predators in the zoo. The most obvious ones were behind bars. Foxes and cats, however, were known to hunt in the grounds. So it seems that the life of a jungle fowl is precarious and its wariness and care in selecting a roost are hardly sufficient protection. Yet a rapid turnover of population is found in many species, and if it were not so and each jungle fowl lived to a ripe old age, life would be hard for flesh-eating animals.

Many animals—songbirds and fishes, for instance—produce large numbers of young; but very few of these survive to reproduce.

Philip Wayre: NHPA

pheasant family. Normally the unmated males hang about the territories of the mated cocks and are extremely secretive, but during the main part of the breeding season they challenge the established cocks by crowing and clapping their wings over their backs. This is a definite challenge and cocks can be lured by imitating the clapping. When fights break out they are fierce and one of the combatants may be severely wounded by the sharp, 1 in. spurs of its adversary.

The cock courts the hen by waltzing around her with one wing lowered to the ground, rubbing the primary feathers of that wing with the nearest foot to produce a rasping sound. The hen makes her nest

from owls and by choosing a perch well out on the most slender branches they reduce the chance of being surprised by such nimble creatures as the palm civet.

Rapid turnover

The jungle fowl's behaviour is very difficult to study in the dense vegetation of its natural home, but it has been studied in detail in semi-wild populations, such as there are at the San Diego zoo. About 150 jungle fowl roam about the zoo grounds in several flocks which have provided a great opportunity for studying their social behaviour. During the course of the study the surprising fact emerged that only 6 out of

If they did, the population would rise enormously and food would run short. Instead, the surplus provide food for flesh-eating animals.

class	**Aves**
order	**Galliformes**
family	**Phasianidae**
genus & species	***Gallus gallus*** *red jungle fowl* ***G. lafayetii*** *Ceylon jungle fowl* ***G. sonnerati*** *grey jungle fowl* ***G. varius*** *green jungle fowl*

Joe Van Wormer

When did the fowl become a chicken?

◁ *An alarmed grey jungle fowl making a hurried retreat. Jungle fowl live in forests in the warmer parts of Asia. As more and more forests are being cut down to make way for agriculture so their range is slowly shrinking. They are managing to survive simply because they are wary birds. Their only defence is to take flight once disturbed.*

△ *Cock and hen red jungle fowl. The scientific name,* **Gallus gallus**, *of this jungle fowl is also the name of the domestic chicken (see page 423), and it is thought that the chicken has been bred from this wild species. This is easy to see from the female which looks quite drab beside her mate. There are other views that the domestic chicken is descended from any one or more of the four species of* **Gallus** *living in southeastern Asia and for this reason some scientists prefer to call it* **Gallus domesticus**. *The time of domestication is unknown although there are Asiatic records of it which go back more than 3 000 years.*

▷ *Map showing the distribution of the four species of jungle fowl.*

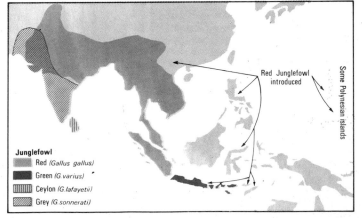

Red Junglefowl introduced

Some Polynesian islands

Junglefowl
- Red *(Gallus gallus)*
- Green *(G. varius)*
- Ceylon *(G. lafayetii)*
- Grey *(G. sonnerati)*

Kallima

This, from a Greek word meaning beautiful, is the generic name of certain butterflies belonging to the family Nymphalidae which are also called leaf butterflies or, more commonly, dead-leaf butterflies. This same family includes the fritillaries, purple emperor, white admiral, and the vanessid butterflies such as peacock, red admiral, tortoiseshell and Camberwell beauty, all brilliantly marked and powerful in flight. The dead-leaf butterflies share these qualities but with the exception that when they close their wings they are transformed. The several species of **Kallima** range from New Guinea through southeast and south Asia to India and Ceylon, with species in Madagascar, the Gold Coast and Ashanti.

The Indian and far eastern species **Kallima inachus** and **K. paralekta** are $3\frac{1}{2}$ in. across the spread wings. The upperside of the wings is patterned with dark brown, blue and bright orange but in the Ceylon species **K. philarchus** the orange is replaced with white. The other species are variously coloured but all have this kind of colour combination.

Bogus foliage

The shape of the wings of kallima butterflies when closed over the back, together with the colours and patterns of their undersides, give the appearance of a dead leaf. Many members of their family have 'tails' on the rear margins of the wings. These are short and blunt-ended. The dead-leaf butterflies have one such tail and when the butterfly comes to rest on a twig this touches the twig and looks like a leaf stalk. The tip of the leaf is represented by the pointed and curved tips of the forewings as they lie together. Between this tip and the bogus leaf stalk runs a dark line, across both fore- and hindwings, which looks just like the midrib of a leaf.

Trembling like a leaf

Less distinct dark lines run obliquely upwards from this central line to the margins of the wings, and these look exactly like the veins of a leaf. To complete the illusion, and this is especially true of K. inachus, the species most often seen in museums or books, there are patches on the wings just like the holes and tears, the fungal growths and other blemishes found on dead leaves. The body, head and antennae are tucked away between the wings when the butterfly is resting and the whole effect is such that once the butterfly has settled it is almost impossible to see it against the background of leaves and branches. No two butterflies of the same species are patterned alike on their underwings, just as no two dead leaves are exactly alike. And immediately the butterfly settles it turns and faces down the stem, as a dead leaf would hang, and it starts to sway gently as if in a breeze.

The celebrated British naturalist AR Wallace met K. paralekta in Sumatra in 1861 and he describes in his book, The Malay Archi-

AB Klots

AB Klots

pelago, how he had the greatest difficulty in finding the butterfly, once it had settled, even when he had watched it fly in and marked the spot with his eye.

Only flies when it must

Dead-leaf butterflies live in regions of heavy rainfall, in thick forests in hilly and mountainous districts. They are seldom seen in the open and never fly far, spending most of their time resting on bushes. When they do fly, as when they are disturbed, they fly off rapidly on an erratic course, the bright colours on the uppersides of their wings making them very conspicuous. The result is they are often chased by birds, but once the butterfly settles and closes its wings the bird chasing it is baffled. The butterfly has done the perfect disappearing act.

Flaunting its colours

The butterflies often settle on sweet sap exuding from trees or on over-ripe fruit or on damp patches on the ground to drink. At such times they hold their wings partly open and move them up and down, with no attempt at concealment.

The disappearing trick

The orange oakleaf, as *K. inachus* is sometimes called, is double brooded. One breeding season is from April to June and the other is after the rains. Its caterpillar feeds on flowering trees and shrubs *Strobilanthus* and *Pseuderantheum*. It is golden brown with nine longitudinal rows of fine spines. Its head and legs are black and on the head are two long red 'horns' set with minute branched spines.

The remarkable resemblance the settled orange oakleaf butterfly bears to a dead leaf has led to this species being used as the last word in perfect protective resemblance. A few entomologists have questioned whether this may not be a mistaken idea because the butterfly usually settles among green foliage, not among dead leaves. On the other hand we have the testimony of Wallace and others that the insect is surprisingly hard to find once it settles. We are on more certain ground in using *Kallima* to illustrate two other principles. The first is that known as *coincident disruptive pattern*. The line which represents the midrib of the leaf runs across the fore- and hindwings, and only forms the unbroken line required for its camouflage effect when the wings are held in the natural position of rest, and this is also true of the leaf-like outline formed by the wings. Any alteration in the relative position of the wings largely destroys the illusion. The other principle is that of *flash coloration*. The upper surface of the wings of *Kallima* are brilliantly coloured orange and blue. When the butterfly suddenly flies there is a startling explosion of bright colour, and when it alights a large blue and orange butterfly apparently disappears, the detailed camouflage of the undersides of its wings seeming to transform it into a dead leaf. Both effects are puzzling and confusing to a predator (or collector) searching for the butterfly, more so than if it had inconspicuous coloration on both upper- and undersides of the wings.

Caric Bevilacqua

◁△ *Museum specimen of* **Kallima inachus**, *uppersides of its wings flaunting the beauty that gave it its name.*

◁ *The underside of the same butterfly — each wing a perfect imitation dead leaf, even to the 'veins' and 'fungus holes' all over it.*

△ *Now you see it: few predators drawn to the bright, flashes of* **Kallima inachus** *in erratic flight can distinguish between butterfly and dead leaf once it has landed.*

▷ *Photographer's reconstruction of* **Kallima inachus** *in typical pose, showing the peak of perfection reached by this insect's camouflage.*

phylum	**Arthropoda**
class	**Insecta**
order	**Lepidoptera**
family	**Nymphalidae**
genus & species	***Kallima inachus, K. paralekta, K. philarchus***

Stephen Dalton: NHPA

Kangaroo

The best-known of the five kangaroos are the great grey and the red. The great grey or forester is up to 6 ft high, exceptionally 7 ft, with a weight of up to 200 lb. Its head is small with large ears, its forelimbs are very small by comparison with the powerful hindlimbs and the strong tail is 4 ft long. The colour is variable but is mainly grey with whitish underparts and white on the legs and underside of the tail. The muzzle is hairy between the nostrils. The male is known as a boomer, the female as a flyer and the young as a Joey. The great grey lives in open forest browsing the vegetation. The red kangaroo is similar to the great grey in size and build but the male has a reddish coat, the adult female is smoky blue, and the muzzle is less hairy. Unlike the great grey kangaroo it lives on open plains, is more a grazer than a browser, and lives more in herds or mobs, usually of a dozen animals.

The 55 species of kangaroo, wallaby and wallaroo make up the family Macropodidae (**macropus** = big foot). Only two are called kangaroos but there are 10 rat kangaroos and two tree kangaroos which, with the wallabies, will be dealt with later. A third species is known as the rock kangaroo or wallaroo. There is no brief way of describing the difference between a kangaroo and a wallaby except to say that the first is larger than the second. An arbitrary rule is that a kangaroo has hindfeet more than 10 in. long.

The red is found all over Australia. The great grey lives mainly in eastern Australia but there are three races of it, formerly regarded as species: the grey kangaroo or western forester of the southwest; that on Kangaroo Island off Yorke Peninsula, South Australia; and the Tasmanian kangaroo or forester. The wallaroo or euro lives among rocks especially in coastal areas. It has shorter and more stockily built hindlegs than the red or the great grey.

Leaps and bounds

When feeding, and so moving slowly, kangaroos balance themselves on their small forelegs and strong tail and swing the large hindlegs forward. They then bring their arms and tail up to complete the second stage of the movement. When travelling fast, only the two hindfeet are used with the tail held almost horizontally as a balancer. They clear obstacles in the same way, with leaps of up to 26 ft long. Usually the leap does not carry them more than 5 ft off the ground but there are reports of these large kangaroos clearing fences up to 9 ft. Their top speed is always a matter for dispute. They seem to be capable of 25 mph over a 300yd stretch but some people claim a higher speed for them.

Eating down the grass

Kangaroos feed mainly by night resting during the heat of the day. The red kangaroo, because it eats grass, has become a serious competitor with sheep, important in Australia's economy. By creating grasslands man has helped the kangaroo increase in numbers. In turn the kangaroo tends to outgraze the sheep, for which the pastures were grown, not only through its increased numbers but by its manner of feeding. Sheep have lower teeth in only the front of the mouth, with a dental pad in the upper jaw. Kangaroos have front teeth in both lower and upper jaw which means they crop grass more closely than sheep. At times, it is reported, they also dig out the grass roots. They can go without water for long periods, which suggests they were originally animals of desert or semi-desert, but where water is supplied for sheep kangaroos will, if not kept out, take the greater share.

Kangaroos set a problem

Enemies of the larger kangaroos are few now that the Tasmanian wolf has been banished. The introduced dingo still claims its victims but that is shot at sight. The loss of natural enemies, the creation of wide areas of grassland and the kangaroo being

◁ *Dusk falls on a kangaroo couple.*

▽ *The despair of Australian graziers, kangaroos let no fence stand between them and their drink.*

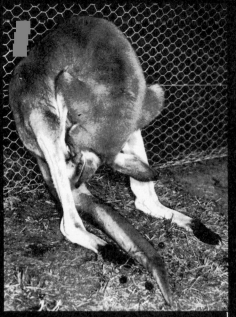

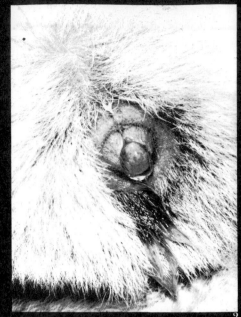

1

2

3

The 33-day gestation over, a red kangaroo cleans her pouch (1) before giving birth (2 and 3) to a $\frac{1}{35}$ oz baby, still in its protective sac, the amnion. Once free of this, but still attached to the umbilical cord, it crawls across the fur (4) until, 3 minutes later, it reaches the pouch (5). Once inside, it takes one of the four teats (three if an older baby is there first) and begins to suckle (6). It will not be weaned for a year, although it leaves the pouch at 8 months; (7) is a 50 day old baby.

4

5

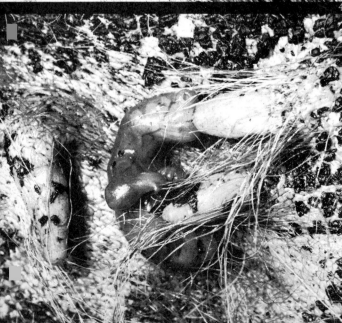

6

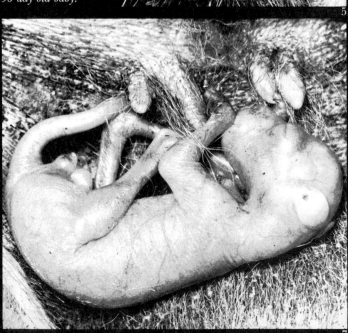

7

able to breed throughout most of the year, has created a problem, especially for sheep graziers, in Australia. Fencing in the pastures, often thousands of acres in extent, is costly—about £200 a mile—and kangaroos have a trick of squeezing under the fence at any weak spot. So kangaroos are shot. In one year, on nine sheep properties totalling 1 540 000 acres, 140 000 kangaroos were shot and it would have needed double this number of kills to keep the properties clear of them. Another problem is that kangaroos often bound across roads at night and collide with cars causing costly damage and endangering those in the cars.

Bean-sized baby

The manner in which baby kangaroos are born and reach the pouch had been in dispute for well over a century. In 1959-60 all doubts were set at rest when the birth process of the red kangaroo was filmed at Adelaide University. About 33 days after mating the female red kangaroo begins to clean her pouch, holding it open with the forepaws and licking the inside. She then takes up the 'birth position' sitting on the base of her tail with the hindlegs extended forwards and her tail passed forward between them. She then licks the opening of her birth canal or cloaca. The newborn kangaroo, ¾in. long, appears headfirst and grasps its mother's fur with the claws on its forefeet. Its hindlegs are at this time very small. In 3 minutes it has dragged itself

to the pouch, entered it and seized one of the four teats in its mouth. The birth is the same for the great grey except that the female stands, with her tail straight out behind her. The baby kangaroo, born at an early stage of development, weighs $\frac{1}{35}$ oz at birth. It remains in the pouch for 8 months, by which time it weighs nearly 10 lb. It continues to be suckled for nearly 6 months after it has left the pouch and can run about, putting its head in to grasp a teat. Meanwhile, another baby has probably been born and is in the pouch. The red kangaroo has lived for 16 years in captivity.

Overlooking the obvious

The truth about kangaroo birth took a long time to be established. In 1629 Francois Pelsaert, a Dutch sea captain, wrecked on the Abrolhos Islands off southwest Australia, was the first to discover the baby in the pouch of a female wallaby. He thought it was born in the pouch. This is what the Aborigines also believed. In 1830 Alexander Collie, a ship's surgeon on a sloop lying in Cockburn Sound, Western Australia, investigated the birth and showed that the baby was born in the usual manner and made its way unaided into the pouch. From then on various suggestions were put forward: that the mother lifted the newborn baby with her forepaws or her lips and placed it in the pouch, or that the baby was budded off from the teat. In 1883 Sir

Richard Owen, distinguished anatomist, came down heavily on the side of those who said the mother placed the baby in her pouch holding it in her lips, yet in 1882 the Hon L Hope had shown Collie to be correct. In 1913 Mr A Goerling wrote a letter to the Perth *Western Mail* describing how he had watched the baby make its way to the pouch with no help from the mother. It was not until 1923, however, that this view was generally accepted, when Dr WT Hornaday, Director of the New York Zoological Gardens, watched and described the birth. Finally, in 1959-60, the whole process of birth was filmed by GB Sharman, JC Merchant, Phyllis Pilton and Meredith Clark, at Adelaide University, setting the matter at rest for all time. It seems so obvious to us now!

class	**Mammalia**
order	**Marsupialia**
family	**Macropodidae**
genus & species	***Macropus giganteus*** *great grey kangaroo* ***M. robustus*** *rock kangaroo or wallaroo* ***M. rufus*** *red kangaroo*

Full steam ahead: a shallow water sprint shows the versatility of bounding movement.

HAE Lucas

G Ruppell

△ *Support from the rear: a red kangaroo resting on his powerful hindlegs and long tail.*

◁ *A place in the sun: a red kangaroo group whiles away a lazy sociable afternoon.*

▷ *Sticking his neck out: Joey investigates the grazing from the warmth of his mother's pouch.*

▽ *Bouncing retreat: great grey kangaroos leaping along on their hindlegs, up to 26 ft at a bound, using their tails as balancers. They can be identified by the black tips to their tails as well as by their large size.*

Kangaroo mouse

There are many species of mice and a fair proportion of these hop or progress in leaps. So it is not surprising that several different species that have specialized in progressing by leaps should have been called kangaroo mice even when they live far from Australia. In Australia itself there are species of mice which some Australian zoologists call hopping mice but the standard textbooks call kangaroo mice. There are also, in this same continent, mice that are not true mice but related to kangaroos. These are sometimes called kangaroo mice and there are 15 of them. These are better called marsupial mice and will be dealt with under that title.

Australia's hopping mice

The kangaroo mice of Australia burrow into sandy soil and are very difficult to dig out because of the speed with which they burrow, and once on the surface they are hard to catch because they hop along so quickly. They are vegetarians, feeding on seeds, leaves and berries. Because they do not compete for food the carnivorous marsupial mice often live in the same burrows as the hopping mice. There are 76 species of true rodents in Australia, not including the introduced ship rat and common rat, and nine of these are variously known as kangaroo mice or hopping mice. They have even been called jerboa mice. They are much the same size, colouring and shape as house mice but their hindlegs are longer in proportion, so the hopping mice look more like jerboas (p 1196). There are 2–5 young in a litter and their life-span is believed to exceed 3 years.

New Guinea's kangaroo mouse . . .

In New Guinea lives another true rodent, a mouse very like the Australian pouched mice. Little is known about its way of life; it is like the Australian hopping mice in size, colour and shape but too little is known of its habits to say whether these compare also with those of the hopping mice.

. . . and more in America

To add to the confusion, there are species in America which are also called pygmy kangaroo rats. They are a lighter colour than the Australian forms but much the same size and they have long hindlegs, a long tail and large ears, and their head is larger in proportion to the body. Another difference is that the soles of the feet are furred, which enables them to hop easily over loose sand. They stay in their burrows by day and come out at night to feed on seeds. In habits they are very like the kangaroo rat, which is discussed separately, especially in their ability to go without water indefinitely, getting the moisture they need from dry seeds. No doubt at times they drink dew or get moisture by eating succulents, but they can do without even these.

The young of both species are born in May or June, in burrows. There are usually 3 or 4 in a litter but there may be as many as 7, and there may be 2 litters a year.

Looking like each other

Although it is highly confusing to have a number of animals known by the same name there is a particular point in bringing them together here, even if each can be discussed but briefly. They illustrate probably better than any other collection of animal species what is known as convergent evolution. By this is meant the principle that animals having the same way of life come to look like each other. All, with perhaps one exception, the New Guinea kangaroo mouse, live under desert or semi-desert conditions in which a hopping or kangaroo-like way of moving over the ground has great advantages. Firstly, in deserts food is scarce and hopping enables an animal to cover ground quickly in search of scanty food. Secondly, hopping is the best way of moving over shifting soil. The jerboas are like them and it is only accidental that they have not been called kangaroo mice—or kangaroo rats, since they are bigger.

There need be little surprise that so many mice should have specialized in leaping. Many animals show a tendency to do so, especially when young. Baby hedgehogs leap into the air when touched. They only leap up a few inches, but then their legs are not strong nor are they built for jumping. When we come to deal with lungless salamanders we shall find there is at least one species that leaps about and a salamander is the last animal we should expect to do this. Rats and mice are almost pre-adapted for this habit. Baby house mice of the wild strain leap about, and so do rats. Some go farther and progress in leaps when adult. It only needs a slight change in their structure, a slight lengthening of the hindlegs and they are already on their way to joining the company of kangaroo mice.

class	**Mammalia**
order	**Rodentia**
family	**Heteromyidae**
genus & species	***Microdipodops megacephalus*** *American*
family	**Muridae**
genera & species	***Lorentzimys nouhuysii*** *New Guinea* ***Notomys filmeri*** *Australian*

▽ *All ears, an apprehensive **Notomys cervinus** backs away from a strange sound.*

Queensland Museum

▽ *Hop-scotch in the sand: kangaroo mice **Notomys fuscus** caught by the flashlight. They spend the day scurrying about in their burrows, coming out at night to feed on berries and fruit.*

F Collet

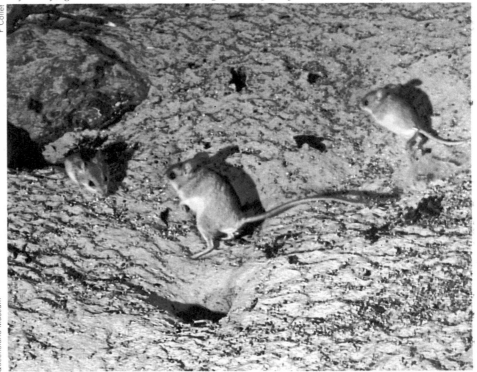

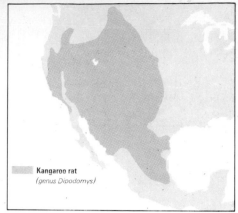

△ *The desert range of the kangaroo rat.*

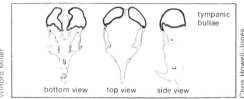

bottom view top view side view

△ *Kangaroo rat skull—adaptation for hearing.*

*Defenceless but for its leaping power, **Dipodomys ordii** waits for a sound to confirm its suspicions.*

Wilford Miller

Chris Howell-Jones

Kangaroo rat

Kangaroo rats are rodents, named for their long hindlegs and tail, short forelegs and leaping gait. They are similar in these respects to jerboas and kangaroo mice, and like these animals they live in deserts. There are 24 species. Their head and body lengths range from 4 to 8 in. with a tail longer than the head and body combined. The fur is pale to dark brown above and white underneath. There is a dark stripe running along the top of the tail, which ends in a tuft of hair.

Kangaroo rats live in North America west of the Missouri, from southwestern California to central Mexico.

Dust bathing for health

Kangaroo rats live in dry or semi-dry country, preferably with sandy soil that they can easily dig and sparse vegetation which favours their bounding method of locomotion. They are nocturnal and will not come out even in moonlight. Wet weather also stops them from coming out.

Dust bathing is apparently very necessary for these animals. Without it they develop sores and their fur becomes matted. Their habits are similar to those of jerboas, as might be expected from their similar form and habitat.

Dry stores

Kangaroo rats can survive long periods without drinking. They obtain their water from dew-soaked and succulent plants but they can also live on dry food like jerboas, getting water from the breakdown of fats and carbohydrates. Their kidneys are very efficient and little water is needed to remove the body wastes.

They eat a variety of plants, including the seeds, leaves, stems and fruits. A few insects are also taken. They collect food in caches for use in times of drought when the sparse vegetation withers up. The kangaroo rats carry the food in their cheek pouches to caches and empty it out, the animal using both forepaws to squeeze the cheeks simultaneously. The pouches are formed from folds of skin and are lined with fur, and stretch back as far as the neck. The kangaroo rats do not merely store their food, they process it first to prevent it going bad. Investigations showed that just after the rainy season the giant kangaroo rat stored seed pods in small pits around its burrow. One kangaroo rat had 875 pits each covered with soil and pressed down. A few months later the pits were empty but the kangaroo rat's burrow contained several large caches of seed pods. It appeared that it was storing its food in shallow pits until it dried out and then transferring it to permanent and more convenient stores. Moreover it was seen to take seed pods that had dried naturally straight to the caches instead of first storing them in pits. Kangaroo rats near grain fields may steal enough grain to be pests.

Breeding by the climate

Kangaroo rats breed at any time of the year providing the climate is suitable. Some breed all the year round, but with few births during the winter months. Gestation lasts 4—5 weeks and the litters consist of 1—5 babies which stay in their mother's burrow for 6 weeks. Each female may bear up to three litters in a year.

Listening for trouble

A feature of any desert-living animals such as elephant shrews, gerbils and jerboas is extremely sensitive hearing. These animals also have very large tympanic bullae, the domed-shaped bones that lie under the base of the skull just beneath the ears. At one time it was thought they acted as resonators that amplified the sounds being transmitted to the inner ears, so allowing these animals to hear very faint sounds.

The function of these bullae and the important role they play in the life of these animals was demonstrated by a series of experiments carried out by Douglas Webster. First he showed that kangaroo rats are extremely sensitive to sounds of frequencies between 1 000 and 3 000 cycles per second. Two mechanisms are involved. Sound waves are transmitted from the eardrum to the sense organs of the inner ear by three small bones in the inner ear. They also amplify the sound, and those of kangaroo rats amplify sound five times more than those in human ears. The large space contained in the auditory bullae was also found to increase the sensitivity of the ear. The enlarged bullae do not act as resonators, but allow the eardrum to vibrate more freely. The eardrum in a normal ear is damped because air pressure builds up behind it in the middle ear, resisting its movements. In the kangaroo rat and other desert animals, the large space inside the bullae easily absorbs any increase in pressure and the eardrum is able to vibrate in response to much weaker vibrations.

Kangaroo rats are preyed on by owls and rattlesnakes and Webster was able to show that the rats can hear their enemies coming and so escape. He placed barn owls or rattlesnakes in a darkened cage and released kangaroo rats onto the floor. As the predator struck the kangaroo rat leaped out of the way. Using sensitive recording equipment Webster was able to detect incredibly faint rustlings from the predators as they pounced, and the rustling sounds were of the frequencies to which kangaroo rats are particularly sensitive. Without these highly sensitive ears the kangaroo rats would be sitting targets. As it is, only a minimal percentage of them are lost to predators.

class	**Mammalia**
order	**Rodentia**
family	**Heteromyidae**
genus & species	***Dipodomys ingens*** giant ***D. merriami*** Merriam's others

Katydid

The name of this American group of bush crickets is at least as well known because of the popularity of a series of girls' books on the theme of What Katy Did . . . *as it is for being the loudest of the grasshoppers. Not only do the katydids make the most strident calls but these have been intensively studied, so shedding valuable light on the whole subject of insect stridulation. These particular American longhorned grasshoppers or bush crickets seem to be calling* 'Katy did, she did', *hence their name, but this is an over-simplification.*

Two of the better known katydids are **Pterophylla camellifolia,** *common in the eastern states, and* **Microcentrum retinerve,** *common in the southern and western states. Katydids feed mainly on leaves, as other bush crickets and grasshoppers do, and their chief enemies are birds. In autumn they lay flattened, slate-coloured eggs laid in two rows along a twig. These hatch the following spring and the nymphs grow by moulting in the usual way (see p 683). The main interest here is in their song and one species in which this has been closely studied is* **Scudderia texensis,** *the Texas bush katydid. This is common on waste lands and fallow fields, on the verges of highways and railway embankments, and wherever weeds and grasses abound. Its range covers the eastern United States. In Florida and southern Georgia it has two generations a year, adults appearing in June and September. In more northerly parts of its range there is probably only one generation a year in early July.*

Songs for separate occasions

Katydids are famed for their sounds, of which there are several different kinds, making up an insect language. The males of the various species of katydids produce two or more different sounds even when on their own and they produce others in response to other males of their own species. The females also make their own sounds. The male Texas bush katydid makes four different sounds, but each of these can be altered according to circumstances. This can be best appreciated by following a day in the life of this katydid.

Tuning up after noon

In the morning and middle of the day the katydid makes no sounds. In the late afternoon and evening he makes short lispy sounds called the fast-pulsed song. This normally lasts less than a minute. At twilight he begins to make a soft ticking sound which can be heard only a few feet away, interspersed with occasional fast-pulses. As darkness sets in a slow-pulsed song is added. Each slow-pulse is followed by a fast-pulse and then a pause, and as the night wears on the fast-pulse gets longer and longer until late at night the fast-pulse may last

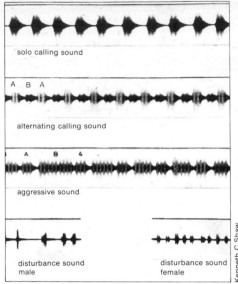

△ *The chirping repertoire of katydid* **Pterophylla camellifolia,** *recorded as patterns. Alone, it sings calmly (top); at another's approach, it quickens, and the insect's songs (A and B) alternate. In the alternating and aggressive sounds, chirps from two different individuals are designated A and B.*

▷ *Fork-tailed katydid* **Scudderia tureata.**

half an hour or more before the slow-pulse is produced. So it is not a simple case of the katydid singing a monotonously produced song, but of a changing song as the light fades at dusk.

Dim lights and soft music

To a large extent the songs of katydids, and presumably of all bush crickets, grasshoppers and true crickets, are influenced by the intensity of light. In many species a low light intensity is needed for them to sing. In others, of which the Texas bush katydid is one, certain sounds are produced principally by day, others in twilight and others in full daylight. In a few species the same sounds are produced by day and by night. The link between different intensities of light is well brought out when a katydid singing in the afternoon in sunlight changes to his twilight song when a cloud passes overhead. Even so, a male of any of these may change his song for a while without any change in the intensity of light. Then, we may presume, it is some change within the insect itself that causes the alteration in the song. Another change comes when one male answers another. Then one calls, waits for the other to answer, then replies, the second one becoming silent to listen for this.

Singing man to man

Generally, bush crickets and grasshoppers that live in dense numbers produce low-intensity songs, that are audible to man at a few feet only. Those well spaced out use louder songs, audible at 200–300 yd. This is reasonable, for where they are close together only a 'whisper' is needed as compared with the 'shout' needed when they are widely separated. In the Texas katydid the male's song changes when another male is moving closer to him. Putting this briefly and in simple terms, the male is first of all

singing to himself. Then as another male moves towards him he advertises the fact he is there and is in effect saying 'Go away'. Finally, if the second male moves in much closer the song becomes a threat.

Talking him in

The last use to which the song is put is to bring male and female together for breeding. In some katydids the male calls and the female who is ready for mating answers him with a ticking call—sometimes it is said that she lisps at him—but stays where she is, he having to go all the way to her. In other species the male sings and the female comes towards him, part of the way, then she begins to tick in answer to his song and he moves over to her, homing on her ticks. There is a third group of species in which when a male calls the female ticks back at him 'come on, then'—and he moves towards her. Having gone so far he changes his tune and stands still. The female now goes the rest of the way to meet him. This is all very different from what we find in other bush crickets and grasshoppers. In these the male sings and the female, who is mute, goes all the way to him.

There may be species of katydid in which both male and female move towards each other at the same time. This is suspected in one species at least, but there is an obvious disadvantage: it is not easy to keep track of a moving sound. We see this principle in operation in the Texas katydid. The male calls and the female ticks her answer and the way she responds, with one, two or three ticks, tells him whether she is fully ready for mating or not. When he receives the maximum response he moves over the bush or plant on which he is perched in her direction. Then he takes wing. If he lands on a bush or plant near her, he calls and she answers, so he takes off again. Once he lands on the same plant as she is on there is silence because she, seeing or feeling him land, sways gently and shakes the plant, so he can find her.

Katydid's hearing aid

Most insects find their mates by seeing each other, as in butterflies, by scent, as in moths, or by being attracted to the same kind of food so they meet there. Few use sounds to bring the sexes together, and of those few the katydids have the most complicated techniques for using sound. We even find that a male katydid will sometimes lean to one side to lift a foreleg and hold it in the air. His ears are on his forelegs, and this action seems to be a definite 'straining to listen'.

phylum	**Arthropoda**
order	**Insecta**
class	**Orthoptera**
family	**Tettigoniidae**
subfamily	**Phaneropterinae**

Kea

The kea is an unusual parrot that is found only in South Island, New Zealand. It is the size of a raven and its plumage has a scaly appearance. In general, keas are olive green with streaks of orange and red on the underparts. The legs are yellow brown and the eyes have yellow pupils that give the kea a beady-eyed look. The bill is nearly 2 in. long and very sharp, but not so curved as in other parrots. It is very strong and the kea is reputed to be able to rip open corrugated iron roofs.

Closely related to the kea is the kaka, which is similar in both habits and appearance. The South Island variety of kaka is larger than that found on the North Island and has a white crown and greenish back instead of a grey crown and predominantly brown plumage with red under the wings. The kaka lives in dense forests and on Kapiti Island there is a kaka sanctuary where they are becoming tame.

In common with all parrots the kea and kaka are very noisy and their names are derived from their harsh calls.

Tin-opener beak

Keas are the hardiest of parrots, sometimes being found in the snow above the treeline. In winter they retreat down the mountain-sides and live in the forests. The kakas live permanently in the forests, lower down. Both live in flocks outside the breeding season. Keas are strong fliers, soaring and gliding gracefully from rock to rock or tree to tree. On the ground they are less agile and move by hopping.

The kea's favourite food is the young leaves and buds of trees but it also walks along the branches tearing off moss, lichen and bark. Feeding is slow and deliberate, the upper half of the powerful bill being used as a lever while the lower half is used as a gouge. When in season, nectar and berries are also eaten. The tongue has a fringe of hairs reminiscent of that on the tongues of honeyeaters (p 1095) and is used to lick nectar from flowers or juice from succulent fruit. Unlike the honeyeater and many other nectar-drinking birds, the keas do not pollinate the flowers they feed upon. Indeed, they destroy the flowers, often chewing them to extract the juices and spitting out the remains.

Grubs and beetles are extracted from the ground and keas also eat flesh. This latter habit is presumed to have developed since sheep were brought to New Zealand. Keas

▽ *Scruffy junior: this gawky bundle of adolescent plumage will grow into an adult, swift and powerful in flight, if a little clumsy on the ground.*

▷▽ *Not-so-pretty Polly: with a wicked glint in its eye, a kea parrot surveys its territory.*

have formed the habit of feeding on carrion and also of tearing open the flesh of living sheep to eat the fat around the kidneys. Tame keas have also been known to eat mice.

Kakas feed on nectar taken up with their brush-tipped tongues, and on berries and other fruits, insects and their larvae.

Nesting under rocks

Keas have very loose territories centred around the nest and roost. Flocks of keas can enter a territory with impunity and the home pair will join them to feed but retire to their own roost at night. Strange keas which are apparently attracted by the calls of the young are tolerated until they come within 25 yd of the nest. The pair then challenge with a cry of 'kua-ua-ua-ua', a call that is also used to challenge man and even vehicles.

Breeding takes place all the year round but mainly in the summer months. The nest of lichens, moss, leaves, ferns and chips of rotten wood is made on the ground, under a boulder, in a crevice, hollow log or among the roots of a tree. There may be an entrance tunnel up to 20 ft long and a well-worn runway and accumulated droppings indicate that the same nests are used year after year. Two to four eggs are incubated for 3–4 weeks. The male kea roosts on a boulder outside the nest and the female joins him there when the chicks are 8 weeks old and filling most of the nest. At first these are helpless and the female feeds them by pushing food into their mouths. After a short time the female loses interest in the chicks and the male has to do all the feeding. The young males become independent 4 weeks after fledging but, for some unknown reason, the adult male continues feeding the young females for another few weeks.

Kakas nest in hollow trees, the female laying four eggs on a layer of powdered wood in a cavity in a tree.

Sheep slaughterers?

Keas have a very bad reputation as sheep killers, perching on the sheep's backs and tearing open their skin to eat the fat and flesh. The wounds themselves may not be severe but poisoning often sets in and leads to death. It is sometimes said that sheep farmers have been put out of business by keas and their reputation has been bad enough for them to be slaughtered by the thousand. In 1886 the Government paid a generous bounty for each beak. The slaughter is still continuing and keas are becoming rare in many places.

Recent researches have, however, suggested that damage by keas is greatly exaggerated and that attacks are mainly made by a few birds that have formed the habit. In some places the burying of offal after slaughtering has reduced the attacks on live sheep as the keas are no longer attracted to the vicinity of the farm. The point has also been made that keas are not very efficient as predators and will wound more sheep than they kill. This means that if keas cause as much damage as they are said to, there must be very large numbers of wounded sheep. Yet one grader who inspected 20–40 thousand fleeces in 10 years never found a single scar from a kea wound. Keas will sometimes settle on humans who encourage them for the fun of it. Very soon the birds begin to peck through their clothes, but as soon as they peck flesh and the victim flinches, the keas fly off. Presumably the same must happen with sheep and the keas are only able to persevere with sick or trapped sheep.

class	**Aves**
order	**Psittaciformes**
family	**Psittacidae**
genus & species	***Nestor meridionalis*** *kaka* ***N. notabilis*** *kea*

Kestrel

The kestrels are small falcons, distributed over all the continents except Antarctica, noted for hovering on gently fanning wings while searching the ground below for prey. In all kestrels the plumage is chestnut and grey with black spots in the male and pale reddish-brown with black streaks and bars in the female.

The common kestrel has numerous races all over Europe, including the British Isles, as well as Asia and Africa. Male and female are about the same size, 13—14 in. long, but the mature male has a grey head while the female and young have brown heads, the young male getting his grey head at 2 years. The American species, called a sparrow-hawk, is very like it. The lesser kestrel,

about a foot long, is now regarded as more nearly related to the red-footed falcons. There are several species on the islands of the Indian and western Pacific Oceans, and the Mauritius kestrel is the rarest of all falcons, down to less than 10 pairs. The largest kestrels are two African species, the greater kestrel and the fox kestrel. Neither of these hovers or they do so very rarely. They catch insects, reptiles and small mammals on the ground.

Hovering for a living

The common kestrel nests and roosts in open woodland but hunts over open country. It also takes up residence in the towers of tall buildings in cities, for example, in the heart of London, feeding mainly on house sparrows and starlings. Besides hovering it takes up position on a perch, on the top of a bush, on a wall or building, on a

post or on telegraph wires and from these vantage points drops to the ground to take prey. When hovering, with head into the wind and tail bent down and fanned, it may glide on the slant to take up a new hovering station, or it may drop to the ground then fly up again to a new position. In straight flight it alternates glides with a few quick wingbeats. The call is a loud 'kee-kee-kee'.

It feeds on mice and voles, small birds, insects and earthworms, and this is typical of all kestrels except the two large African species. Insects taken are mainly large beetles, moths and grasshoppers. The proportion of these foods taken depends much on the season and on local abundance. For example, it is not unusual for a kestrel to spend an hour or more hovering over one field, dropping to earth every now and then, eating nothing but butterflies and moths. At another time a kestrel may spend long periods dropping from a post and back again taking nothing but earthworms.

◁ *'Mantling': disturbed just before a meal, an irate kestrel threatens the intruder.*   △ *Clumsy homecoming: wings and legs akimbo, a kestrel makes an awkward arrival at its nest.*   ▽ *Kestrel about to feed a large rodent to a hungry family. The chicks fledge in a month.*

Kestrels also take carrion, such as large bird carcases, and both the European and the American kestrels have been seen taking meat scraps and bread from bird tables. They will also rob other birds of prey: one kestrel flew to a barn owl carrying a vole, turned on its back under the owl, seized the vole in its talons and then flew away.

Aerial courtship

Courtship, in late March or early April, consists of aerial displays by the male flying in circles over the perched female. Throughout his displays he flies with 3 or 4 wingbeats followed by a glide, repeated as if part of a ritual, and calling 'kee-kee-kee', all the time. Every so often he flies at the female, not stooping at her but buzzing her, pulling out of his dive at the last moment to fly up and circle her again. Sometimes she flies up and he continues these same manoeuvres over and around her. Kestrels make no nest so the 4–6 eggs, white with blotches of dark red-brown, are laid at intervals of 2 days in the abandoned nest of a large bird such as a crow, in a crevice in a building or on a ledge on a cliff or in a hollow tree. Incubation is mainly by the female, the male bringing her food, but he does sit sometimes. The eggs hatch in a month, the nestlings being brooded by the hen while her mate continues to bring

◁△ *In its element: riding wind and rising air, a kestrel patrols late summer fields.*

△△ *An American sparrowhawk awaits the tiny movement which will betray its next victim.*

△ *Slumming: kestrel and nest in Central London. With the mice and sparrows of Regent's Park only a minute's flying time away, the chick (right) is well fed in its avian hovel.*

food. The babies fledge at 4–4½ weeks, but are fed for a further period after fledging. When they finally go the nest is littered with pellets regurgitated by the young birds.

Lashing out at intruders

The defence reaction of young kestrels is to throw themselves on their backs, presenting two sets of talons to an intruder. When the intrusion is a human hand the talons take firm hold of it and the bird will continue to cling even when lifted up. Then the beak is brought into action as well. Little is known of the enemies of kestrels but this defence reaction of the young, shared by other birds of prey including owls, is probably sufficient to keep most predators at bay. Deaths are mainly accidental, like the kestrel that flew down to seize a vole just as a weasel was about to do the same. The weasel killed the kestrel. Sometimes a kestrel will seize a weasel in its talons, and be bitten fatally by its intended victim.

Kestrel's keen sight

The kestrel, or windhover as it is sometimes called, may hover at heights of a few to 100 ft or more, moving its head from side to side scanning the ground beneath. At the same time it is not unaware of movement to the side as shown by a simple instance which also brings out the keen eyesight of falcons. A kestrel was hovering over a field when it suddenly glided to its right to the top of a tall oak 200 yd away. A human observer watching the kestrel, a similar distance from the oak, could see nothing, with his naked eye, on the foliage of the oak to attract the kestrel. When he brought his binoculars up, however, he could see that the kestrel had taken a small white butterfly in his beak.

class	**Aves**
order	**Falconiformes**
family	**Falconidae**
genus & species	***Falco alopex*** *fox kestrel*
	F. naumanni *lesser kestrel*
	F. punctatus *Mauritius kestrel*
	F. rupicoloides *greater kestrel*
	F. sparverius
	American sparrowhawk
	F. tinnunculus *common kestrel*
	others

Killdeer

A common plover of America, the
killdeer, named after its call, breeds on
inland pastures and meadows. It is 10 in.
long, rather larger than the related
ringed plovers but similar in plumage.
The upperparts are bright chestnut and
the underparts white. The forehead and
breast have conspicuous white bands.
There are two bands on the breast compared with the single band on the ringed
plover and the semipalmated plover.
The long legs are straw-coloured and
the bill black.

The killdeer breeds from Canada to
Chile, including the West Indies. The
northern population migrates south for
the winter and occasional stragglers find
their way across the Atlantic, although
less than two dozen have been recorded
in the British Isles.

hour at a time. All the while they are in the air they give voice to a continuous musical trill. On the ground the female is courted with a display in which the male lowers his spread wings on the ground and fans his tail over his back.

The nest is no more than a depression in the ground lined with a few pebbles and other bits and pieces. Killdeer prefer to nest on stony ground, in meadows or cultivated fields, where the ground is bare and usually fairly near water. Unusual nesting places include the ballast between railway sleepers, a tar and gravel roof and a rubbish heap of old bottles and tins. The eggs are 3—5 in number, pale brown with brown or black irregular marks. Both parents incubate the eggs for 25—26 days and both guard the young birds which leave the nest shortly after they have hatched.

Feigning injury

The eggs and chicks of killdeer are extremely well-camouflaged, as is the rule among ground-nesting birds, but the adults make the nest or young even more difficult to find by luring predators away with distraction displays. Distraction displays are common among ground-nesting birds, especially waders. The most usual display is that known as 'injury feigning' where the parent gives a passable imitation of a bird with a broken wing and lures a predator, such as a fox, away from its brood then flies up just before it is attacked. A description of a curlew luring a coyote for half a mile is given on page 595.

It must not be thought that the bird is consciously trying to deceive its enemies. The display is probably caused by a conflict between an urge to defend the brood and an urge to fly away to safety, the result being a strange action that attracts the attention of the enemy. If anyone walks near the nest of a killdeer, one or other of the parents drops to the ground with one wing held over its back, the other beating against the ground and the tail fanned. The combination of movements and displaying the white on wings and tail make the killdeer very conspicuous. As it is approached, it runs normally a little way and repeats the performance. This is repeated until the intruder is about 100 yd from the nest when the killdeer flies off.

When confronted with grazing animals, such as cattle and sheep, that are dangerous only because they may trample the brood, the killdeer's reaction is different. They stand over the nest or young with wings outspread and quivering, calling vigorously. So effective is this that a flock of goats were once seen to part, each group running either side of the killdeer's nest.

△ *Alone with its reflection, a killdeer scours the shallows for anything unfortunate enough to move.*

Joe van Wormer; Photo Res

Hard to see, easy to hear
Outside the breeding season killdeer live in flocks, inland or along the shore. Despite their apparently striking plumage with the black bands contrasting with the white background, the flocks of killdeer are difficult to see, and because they are quite tame one can sometimes walk almost up to a flock before noticing them. The black bands are an example of a 'disruptive pattern', breaking up the outline of the body and making it difficult to see. By contrast killdeer are very noisy, as indicated by the scientific name *Charadrius vociferus*. Its English name is derived from its call note 'kill-dee', with a final 'r' added. When disturbed killdeer fly very rapidly, not far off the ground, and they can also run very rapidly.

Beneficial bird
The flocks of killdeer feed scattered over the ground rather than in a compact bunch, eating insects and other small animals. They follow the plough to catch the animals thrown to the surface or search among grass or low plants. In one study, two-thirds of the animals found in killdeers' stomachs were insects, of which one-third were beetles. There were also grasshoppers, caterpillars, flies, ants, weevils and bugs among the other insects found, and there were also centipedes, ticks, earthworms and snails. Many of the insects taken are pests, such as weevils, wireworms and caterpillars. Killdeer are one of the most important predators of the cotton boll weevil, one killdeer being found with 380 weevils in its stomach. Grasshoppers are also eaten in large numbers and killdeer have earned a good name through eating mosquito larvae and cattle ticks.

Nesting on pebbles
Male killdeer have a spectacular aerial display. They fly back and forth or climb in spirals, sometimes hovering, for up to an

class	**Aves**
order	**Charadriiformes**
family	**Charadriidae**
genus & species	***Charadrius vociferus***

Killer whale

The killer whale is closely related to the false killer whale (p 735) and the pilot whale. It has a very bad reputation for ferocity which is probably unjustified. Killer whales are small for whales, the females growing up to a maximum of about 15 ft, but an old male may be as long as 30 ft. They are one of the few whales in which there is a marked difference in size between the sexes, the sperm whale being another example. The colour is very striking and distinctive, both sexes having similar markings, which are black on the back and white on the underside. Occasionally the white is some-what yellowish. The chin is white and there is a characteristic white oval patch just above and behind the eye. There is a small whitish patch just behind the dorsal fin which varies quite considerably in shape and hue in different animals. The white on the underside sweeps up towards the tail and the flanks are white between the dorsal fin and the tail. The flippers, which are broad and rounded, are black all over, but the underside of the tail flukes are white. The dorsal fin is very conspicuous, usually about 2 ft high, but in the old males it may be 6 ft. The oldest males also have very long flippers, up to $\frac{1}{5}$ the animal's total length, the average length of the flipper in juvenile males and adult females being $\frac{1}{9}$ only.

Killer whales are found in all seas but are particularly numerous in the Arctic and Antarctic where there is abundant food to satisfy their voracious appetite. They are not uncommon around the British Isles, where a number have been stranded, mainly on the north and east coasts. These strandings take place in most months of the year. A larger number than usual were stranded on British coasts during the last war, mostly on the North Sea coast, probably due in part at least to anti-submarine activities.

Living in packs

Killer whales hunt together in packs made up of both sexes. They are inquisitive and appear to take a close interest in anything likely to be edible. Nothing is known about their movements in the oceans or how much, if at all, the populations in different oceans mix. In the Antarctic they are often seen around whaling factory ships and probably they tend to follow the ships around as they offer an easy source of food. Otherwise very little is known about their habits.

Ruthless hunters

The killer whale is a voracious feeder and will take anything that swims in the sea. Included in its diet are whales, dolphins, seals, penguins, fish and squid. It will attack even the large blue whales and quite often killers will hunt in packs numbering from two or three up to as many as 40 or more. When attacking a large whale they are said to work as a team. First one or two will seize the tail flukes to stop the whale thrashing about and slow it down, then others will attack the head and try to bite the lips. Gradually the whale becomes exhausted and its tongue lolls from its mouth—to be immediately seized by the killers. At this point all is over for the whale: the tongue is rapidly removed and the killers take their fill, seeming to favour a meal from around the head of their monster victim.

Apart from attacking fully-grown and healthy whales, killers have earned the hate of whalers because they often take the tongues from whales that have been harpooned and are lying alongside the factory ship waiting to be processed. They will even take the tongue from whales being towed by the catcher boat, and in an effort to stop this looting a man may be posted with a rifle to deter the killers. If he should injure a killer all the others in the pack turn on it and it very soon becomes their next meal.

Killer whales also eat seals and porpoises, and there are a number of records of complete seals found in a killer's stomach. The greatest number recorded is the remains of 13 porpoises and 14 seals that were taken from the stomach of one killer whale, while another contained 32 full-grown seals. Off the Pribilof Islands in the Bering Sea, killer whales are often seen lying in wait for the young fur seal pups swimming out into the open sea for the first time. The number of seals actually taken by killers is not certain but it is likely that large numbers of pups must meet their end in this way before they reach the age of one year.

In the Antarctic, penguins form an important part of the killer whale diet. On many occasions killer whales have been seen swimming underneath ice floes, either singly or sometimes several at a time, and then coming up quickly under the floe either to tip it or break it up, thereby causing the penguins to fall into the water and into the waiting jaws of the killers.

Once killer whales were seen cruising close to an island where there was a colony of grey seals. As the killers came close in the seals hurried ashore in spite of a couple of people standing nearby. The certain danger from killer whales was more important to the seals than possible danger from man. It is said that when killer whales

△ *Running at the surface with blowhole open, a killer whale in relaxed mood.*

△ *Affectionate play between a pair of killers. Sensory pits can be seen on the head.*

attack grey whales, these become so terrified that they just float on their backs unable to make any effort to escape.

Seven-footer calves

Very little is known about the breeding habits of the whale. They are thought to produce their young towards the end of the year, in November and December after a 16-month gestation. This is supported by examination of some of the stranded whales washed up on the beach and found to be pregnant. The calf at birth is about 7 ft long. The females suckle the young in the same way as other whales, but how long this lasts is not known.

No enemies

The killer whale probably has no real enemies. A few are killed by man, usually irate whalers. They are not a very valuable catch to a whaler although some Russian whaling fleets do catch a few, usually if there is nothing else worth shooting.

Chased by killers

The most famous story of killer whales is that told by Herbert Ponting who was the official photographer to the British *Terra Nova* Antarctic expedition led by Captain Scott in 1911. While the ship's cargo was being unloaded onto the ice some killer whales appeared nearby. Ponting went to take some photographs carrying the bulky photographic apparatus of those days over the floes. As he went across the ice the killers thrust up alongside and then followed him as he crossed the floes, tipping them from beneath. Ponting just managed to get to the safety of the fast ice in front of the killers—a lucky escape.

Ponting's experience must have been terrifying, yet it is often found that a reputation for ferocity is unfounded. Divers who have met killer whales have not been molested and several killer whales have been kept in oceanaria. All have been unaggressive or even hand-tame. One story goes of a fisherman of Long Island, New York, who threw a harpoon at a killer whale. The whale pulled free and followed the boat and its terrified occupants to shallow water, but it made no attempt to harm them despite such severe provocation.

class	**Mammalia**
order	**Cetacea**
family	**Delphinidae**
genus & species	***Orcinus orca***

◁ *Flukes aloft, a killer sounds with a minimum of splash—a tribute to its streamlining.* △ *A killer pack surges round the edges of encroaching ice.* ▽ *Killer curiosity.*

Photos: Brit Antarctic Survey

◁ *Female king crab blunders through the sand with two males in tow.*

▽ *Creature from the past, as its underside shows.*

L Lee Rue III: Photo Res

AB Klots

King crab

The king crab, sometimes called horse-shoe crab, is not a crab but more nearly related to spiders. It hardly looks like a crab either. It looks more like something out of the past, which is what it is: a living fossil. Seen from above on a sandy shore, it appears to be made up of a rounded brown or dark olive-green dome hinged to a hard and roughly triangular abdomen, ending in a long, movable tail spike. The whole animal may be anything up to 2 ft long. When turned over to expose the underside, the dome, or carapace, is seen to have a horseshoe outline sheltering a series of pairs of jointed limbs. Behind the first short pair are four pairs of longer limbs, all alike. All these limbs end in little pincers except for the second pair (or second and third pairs, according to species) in the adult male. Next in the series is one more pair of legs with no pincers. Instead there are spines which spring from the last joint but one and help the animal in getting a grip on the sand. Finally, on this front part of the body is a pair of small structures of uncertain function, known as chilaria. The series is continued on the abdomen, first with a sort of cover or operculum with the paired genital openings on its under-surface, and then five pairs of flaps or 'gill books', so-called because each one is made of up to 200 thin leaflets. These are the gills.

*Of the five species, **Limulus polyphemus** lives on or near the shore in sounds, bays and estuaries down the Atlantic coast of North America from the Gulf of Maine to the Gulf of Mexico. It is especially common in Long Island Sound and the mouth of the Delaware river. In places it is so common it has been caught in large numbers, ground up and used either as*

a fertilizer or as chicken feed. The other four species live far distant, along the coasts of Asia from Japan and Korea south to the Philippines and the East Indies and the Bay of Bengal.

Living sand plough

The tail-spike of the king crab, an innocuous and far from agile animal, is not the weapon it seems, but is used as a lever when its owner is ploughing through sand or mud. It is also used as a lever to right itself, on the rare occasions when it has been turned over by the waves. Much of the time a king crab rests partly or completely buried. There are two eyes to the side and a third eye in the middle further forward on top of the carapace. Digging and ploughing through sand is accomplished mainly by the last pair of legs, those in front serving more to lift the animal, while the last pair pushes backwards like a pair of ski sticks. The crab is also able to swim upside down in a leisurely manner by flapping its gill books, an action also important in circulating water amongst the leaflets.

Chewing with its legs

Although it may eat seaweed, the king crab eats mainly molluscs and worms and it is sometimes a serious predator on clam beds on the American coast. The mouth is on the underside, surrounded by the legs, and the basal joints of the legs have spiny protuberances used to chew food.

Coming ashore to breed

The American king crab breeds early in summer, when the moon is full and the tides deepest. The females, which are the larger, creep up the beach each with a male clinging to her abdomen. They scoop depressions in the sand near the limit of high tide and deposit in these 200−300 eggs, each $\frac{1}{5}$ in. diameter, and covered with a thick envelope. As they are laid the males fertilise them. The eggs are covered with sand and then the males and females go their separate ways. After about a month a short-tailed larva, about $\frac{1}{25}$ in. long, hatches.

It looks superficially like a tiny trilobite, the crustacean that flourished millions of years ago, and for that reason it is called a 'trilobite larva'. It is not until the third year, after the larva has shed its shell more than a dozen times, that sexual maturity is reached. On the other side of the world, when the king crabs come ashore to breed in July and August in the Gulf of Tonkin, they are caught and eaten by the local in-habitants. Europeans tend to find them sickening and it is said that the flesh can be poisonous under certain conditions.

A class of their own

Though called 'crabs', these animals are not only not true crabs, they are not even crustaceans. Like the crustaceans, insects, spiders and other animals with external skeletons and jointed limbs, they are classified as arthropods, but, within that phylum, few as they are, they belong in a class of their own. Their occurrence in two regions so far apart, separated by waters in which they are not suited to survive, suggests that they are relics of a more widespread group, rather than that they are members of a group still in the process of extending its range. That this is so, is supported by the existence of fossils in Bavaria, in the Upper Jurassic. King crabs very like those living today have existed for practically two hundred million years. Animals looking, as adults, somewhat like the king crab larva inhabited the earth even before that. Another group of animals which they re-semble in some ways but which they have long outlived, was the extinct eurypterids, scorpion-like aquatic animals that some-times reached a length of 10 ft. Despite the resemblance of their larvae to them, king crabs are only distantly related to trilobites.

phylum	**Arthropoda**
class	**Merostoma**
order	**Xiphosura**

Kingfisher

There are over 80 species of kingfisher living mainly in the tropics. They are stockily built with long bills, quite short tails and often brilliant plumage, of which the common kingfisher of Europe and Asia is a good example. The well known kookaburra or 'laughing jackass' of Australia, another of the family, is treated under a separate heading. The common kingfisher is found throughout much of Europe and Asia, south into North Africa and east to the Solomon Islands and Japan. It is one of the most beautiful British birds, 6½ in. long with a 1½in. dagger-like bill, its upperparts a shining iridescent blue or green.

▷ *Psychedelic forest kingfisher of Malaya.*

▽ *A giant kingfisher* **Megaceryle maxima** *glares from a vantage point over a stream.*

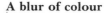

FGH Allen

◁ ▽ *Malachite kingfisher* **Corythornis cristata**, *a very common African species. It feeds on fish, water invertebrates and flies.*

A blur of colour

Kingfishers are usually seen as little more than a blur of colour as they fly low over the water on whirring wings to disappear into waterside undergrowth. If lucky one sees it perched on a branch, rock or post on the bank and its true colours can then be appreciated. Kingfishers are very much alike in habit as well as form; their feeding and breeding behaviour follow a pattern although some kingfishers rarely, if ever, go near water. Even the common kingfisher, associated so much with streams and rivers, sometimes nests some distance from water.

When thousands of exotic birds were being slaughtered and their carcases and feathers sent to Europe and North America as decorations and ornaments, it is not surprising that the dazzling kingfisher did not escape persecution. It was used for decorating hats and stuffed kingfishers in

Peter Johnson

Peter Johnson

Keystone

▷ *King of the world: perched aloft, a grey-headed kingfisher* **Halcyon leucocephala** *watches carefully for passing insects. It also feeds on beetles, grasshoppers and small reptiles.*

The underparts are chestnut, the legs red and there are patches of white on the neck. The pied kingfisher of Africa south of the Sahara and southwest Asia is dull-coloured for a kingfisher but is nevertheless striking with its black and white plumage. Like many kingfishers it has a crest. The Amazon kingfisher, also crested, has brilliant green upperparts and white underparts, with a chestnut breast in the male. The Texas kingfisher, ranging into the southern USA, is very similar. In some species where the sexes differ in plumage, the female is the more brilliant. On the other side of the Pacific the yellow sacred kingfisher is found in many parts of Australia and is the only kingfisher in New Zealand.

RT Peterson: Photo Res

△ *Forest kingfisher* **Halcyon macleyi** *peers from its nesting hole in a termite nest on the side of a eucalyptus tree. This species is an insect-eater, living in Australia.*

glass cases were a common household ornament. Later kingfishers were shot because they were alleged to eat enough trout fry to damage breeding stocks. The pollution of rivers and streams now threatens their wellbeing. Hard winters have a very severe effect on kingfisher populations.

Fishing over land and water

The method of catching prey is similar in nearly all species. The kingfisher waits on a perch, then darts out, catches its prey and carries it back to its perch. The common kingfisher flies out, hovers momentarily just over the water then dives in. Having caught a small fish or water insect it uses its wings to 'fly' through the water then up into the air without pausing. Larger prey are beaten against the perch to subdue them and may be tossed and caught again to get them into

Flying piledriver
Kingfishers hollow out their nesting burrow in the side of a river bank by flying straight at it to chip away the earth.

1 Kingfisher flies straight at its burrow.

2 Nose up and into the vertical, the kingfisher positions itself for landing.

3 Into neutral as it folds its wings well back.

4 With all the feathers splayed, the last-minute air brakes are applied.

5 The kingfisher lands on the edge of the burrow to scoop out more earth from the inside.

The blue torpedo
From a post above the water the kingfisher dives and surfaces in one fell swoop. (Series of stills from 16mm ciné film by the Eastmans.)

6 On spotting a fish, a kingfisher plummets downwards through the water.

7 Using its wings as fins, it torpedoes towards its prey . . .

8 . . . surrounded by a mass of bubbles.

9 Right on target, it grabs its fish and, without a moment's pause . . .

10 . . . returns triumphantly.

◁*Common kingfisher with prospective meal.*

Series by Ron & Rose Eastman

Werner Curth

a suitable position for swallowing. Common kingfishers take mainly fish such as minnows, sticklebacks and gudgeon, also small perch and small trout. These last two are the reason for the persecution of kingfishers, but they also feed on water beetles, dragonfly larvae and waterboatmen which also kill small fish. Small frogs, tadpoles and pond snails are also taken.

The majority of kingfishers, however, take mainly land animals, although they hunt from a perch like the common kingfisher. They dart down from their perches like shrikes or they hawk passing insects like flycatchers. The racquet-tailed kingfisher, living in the area from the Moluccas to northeast Australia, hunts for lizards, centipedes and insects in the leaf litter of humid forests, swooping on them and sometimes driving its bill into the soft earth. The stork-billed kingfisher of India, 14 in. long with a large scarlet bill, catches fish as well as frogs, lizards, crabs and insects. It also robs other birds' nests, taking nestlings even from nests in holes in trees, but, true to its kind, it returns to its perch to swallow its prey. An exception to this is the shoe-billed kingfisher of the forests of New Guinea. It digs for earthworms with its flattened bill.

Hole nesting
Kingfishers nest in holes, those that hunt fish usually nesting in holes in banks near water while the more land-living kingfishers nest in holes in trees or abandoned termite nests. The striped kingfisher of Africa uses ready-made holes and may even dispossess swallows from their nests under eaves.

The nest hole is dug by the kingfishers repeatedly flying at one spot on the bank, loosening a bit of soil with their bills each time. When they have formed a ledge they can perch and dig more rapidly until the tunnel is 1½–3 ft long. The 6 or 7 spherical white eggs are laid on the floor of the tunnel and incubated for 3 weeks. During this time a revolting pile of fish bones and droppings piles up around the eggs, a squalid contrast with the magnificent plumage of the adult birds. Until Ron and

Rose Eastman made their prizewinning film 'The Private Life of a Kingfisher' in 1966 it was thought that pieces of fish were fed to the young. Their remarkable patience and technique, however, showed the young inside the nest burrow swallowing whole fish almost as big as themselves, the bones being later regurgitated. The chicks, which live in the tunnel for 3–4 weeks, are hatched naked but soon acquire a covering of bristle-like wax sheaths which are shed to reveal a plumage like that of the parents just before they leave the nest.

Halcyon days

The kingfisher has been the subject of many legends, some romantic and some prosaic. In the 12th century it was thought that not only did they not decay when dead but that the corpses, if hung up by the bill, moulted each year to reveal a fresh plumage. The odour of these miraculous corpses was said to be pleasant and to ward off moths. A dead kingfisher suspended from a string pointed north like a compass needle or, according to another version, towards the way of the wind. The habits of kingfishers, according to the Ancients, were most remarkable. Their Greek name was Halkyon, literally

meaning 'conceiving at sea'. It was thought that the female fed and conceived at sea and laid her eggs at midwinter in a nest that was so hard that it could not be cut by iron. She was supposed to have incubated the eggs for 2 weeks and fed the chicks for another fortnight. Being in the favour of the gods the weather was kept calm for this period at midwinter, which has ever since been known as the 'halcyon days'.

class	**Aves**
order	**Coraciiformes**
family	**Alcedinidae**
genera & species	*Alcedo atthis* common kingfisher *Ceryle rudis* pied kingfisher *Chloroceryle amazona* Amazon kingfisher *C. americana* Texas kingfisher *Clytoceyx rex* shoe-billed kingfisher *Halcyon chelicuti* striped kingfisher *H. sancta* sacred kingfisher *Pelargopsis capensis* stork-billed kingfisher *Tanysiptera galatea* racquet-tailed kingfisher

Kingfishers
(family Alcedinidae)

▽ *A squad of scruffy young belted kingfishers* **Megaceryle alcyon** *in a hungry line. They swallow small fish whole, regurgitating the bones.*

Photo Researchers

King penguin

King penguins look very much like emperor penguins, to which they are very closely related. They have the same stately walk as the emperors, with their long knife-shaped bills held up. King penguins are the smaller of the two, 3 ft long instead of 4 ft, but are otherwise similar in appearance. They both have blue-black backs and white fronts with yellow and orange patches around the neck, but in the king penguin the patches are separated into two comma-shapes on the side of the neck with a 'bib' of yellow on the breast.

King penguins live farther north than emperor penguins, in the ice-free sub-Antarctic seas between the Falkland Islands southwards to the South Sandwich Islands and Heard Island. There are very small colonies on Staten Island, near Cape Horn, and on the Falkland Islands. The largest colonies are found on islands such as South Georgia, Kerguelen, Macquarie and Marion.

Life on the Antarctic wave

▽ *The king penguins are quite at home in the sea, and when they are not breeding spend much of their time swimming and diving for food. They have streamlined bodies and sharp lethal bills which they use to catch squid and fish. The wings of these birds are modified for use as underwater flippers. The only remaining wing plumage is scale-like feathers which offer little resistance to water.*
▷ *King penguins do not make a nest but the single egg is incubated by the parents putting it on their feet and covering it with an abdominal fold of skin.*
▽▽ *Freshly moulted king penguins proudly displaying their magnificent new coats.*
▷▷ *A superb picture taken in South Georgia.*
▷▽ *A well-ordered colony of king penguins each with its own little territory.*

Jochen Köhler: Bavaria

*Yetis of the Antarctic! The little sheath bill **Chionis** is dwarfed by the big brown penguin chicks.*

B Tollu : Jacana

Feeding at sea

Like other penguins, king penguins live at sea when they are not breeding and sometimes swim long distances, turning up on the fringes of the Antarctic pack ice. The latitudes in which the king penguins live are those of the roaring westerly gales, but these are unlikely to affect the penguins much except to drive them off course. Penguins are perfectly adapted to life at sea. Their bodies are streamlined and a layer of blubber under the skin insulates them from the cold water. The large king and emperor penguins can dive to considerable depths to hunt squid and fish which they catch in their sharp bills. The eyes of aquatic animals are designed to see underwater. Light is not bent so much as it passes from water into the eye as when it passes from air. To compensate, the lens is very strong. As a result aquatic animals are short-sighted out of water.

Prolonged childhood

The king penguin has the same problem of child care as the emperor penguin. Both are very large birds and their chicks take a long time to grow, yet the Antarctic summer is very short. The emperor penguin, as we have seen (p 723), has solved the problem by starting the 7-month nursery period in midwinter so the chicks become independent before the following winter. The king penguin has a different method. It lives farther north where the sea does not freeze and the adults are able to feed near the colony. So instead of laying their eggs in midwinter, the king penguins lay in spring or summer and when the chick hatches after 7½ weeks it is fed throughout the following winter, becoming independent the next summer.

Just before they start breeding king penguins come ashore to moult. They spend a fortnight ashore shedding their old feathers to reveal the brilliant new coat, then retire to sea to feed and build up reserves of food before breeding. Returning to land, they make their way to the colony among the tussack grass and mud where each male takes up position and advertises for a mate. He stretches his neck, ruffs out his feathers and tilts his head back and calls, braying like a donkey. If an unmated female hears him, she wanders over and the two penguins introduce themselves by flagging their bills up and down. They then set off on an 'advertisement walk', strutting along on their toes, waving their heads from side to side, showing off their brilliant patches of colour. The colours are important—if they are covered with black paint a penguin stands no chance of getting a mate.

At first these partnerships do not last very long. The male displays at any female and keeps company with a succession of prospective mates. Gradually, however, he pays attention to one particular female and the bond between them strengthens and they perform another display; standing side by side they raise their beaks and stand on their toes as if stretching themselves.

The king penguin, like the emperor penguin, makes no nest but balances the single large egg on his feet, protected by a fold of skin. He does, however, defend a small territory rather than wander about with his egg. The first eggs are laid in November, and more are laid until April. After laying the female goes off to feed and make up the food reserves she lost forming the egg. The male is left guarding the egg until the female's return 2 weeks later. Thereafter, there is a shuttle service, each parent taking a turn in guarding the egg or chick.

As the chicks get older they spend more time on their own and eventually form creches where they huddle together while parents go fishing. On its return a parent king penguin finds its chick by sound. It walks up to the crèche and calls, and one chick out of hundreds replies. They both walk towards each other, calling, and may even walk past, until another call brings them back to each other. Several pounds of food are transferred at each feed and the chicks put on weight rapidly, but as winter sets in feeding becomes very infrequent and the chicks huddle in their crèches, protected by their thick, woolly down but gradually losing weight. Then, in spring, when food becomes abundant again, the chicks put on weight, lose their down and the adult plumage emerges.

The chicks take to the sea 2 months later and learn to fish for themselves. This is well-timed because food is abundant at this season. The young king penguins stay at sea for most of their early life, spending more time ashore as they get older and begin to practise their courtship displays. At 6 years old, they come ashore and start courting in earnest.

Boiled for blubber

The enemies of king penguins are leopard seals. They lie in wait off the colonies, but the seals will find them difficult to catch as the penguins have an alarm system. When a king penguin sees a leopard seal, it panics and rushes towards the shore. Its flippers beat on the surface of the water and the clattering sound they make alerts other king penguins, and they all rush clattering to the shore. Not only are all the penguins alerted but the leopard seals are probably confused and will be able to catch only weak or unwary penguins.

At one time, man was a far greater enemy. As elephant and fur seals became scarce sealers killed king penguins for their blubber, which was used for tanning leather. Their eggs were taken and their skins sometimes used for fancy clothing. Some colonies were wiped out and others are only just beginning to recover their former numbers.

Slow breeding

It took only a few years for the sealers to reduce the numbers in a king penguin colony to such an extent that it was not worth their while to exploit them further. The reason for this is the extremely slow rate of breeding. After the egg has been laid, a pair of king penguins spends a year incubating, guarding or collecting food. By the time they are free of their offspring it is too late in the year to begin again and they leave the colony to feed during the winter and start breeding the following spring.

Therefore, king penguins, like the larger albatrosses (p 24) which also spend their first winter on the nest, cannot raise more than one young every two years. Furthermore, not all their offspring survive the first winter. If the egg is laid too late in the summer the chick will not have had time to accumulate enough fat with which to survive the winter. Without the attentions of the sealers, king penguins flourish; they are long-lived and generally survive to rear enough offspring to keep numbers constant.

class	**Aves**
order	**Sphenisciformes**
family	**Spheniscidae**
genus & species	*Aptenodytes patagonica*

John Tashjian at Arizona Sonara Desert Mus.

Lampropeltis getulus splendida, Sonora king snake, has distinctive black marks along its back.

King snake

These are North American snakes, harmless to man—as are most members of their large family, the Colubridae. A special feature of king snakes—and the reason why they are so named—is that they eat other snakes, including venomous species like rattlesnakes. Another feature is that they show many colour varieties.

The common king snake, also known as the chain snake or thunder snake, is up to 6 ft long. The typical form, along the east coast area of the United States, is shiny black, criss-crossed by bands of yellow or white forming a chain-like pattern on its sides. Its underside is black with white or yellow blotches. The head is narrow and there is a slightly marked neck. In the Mississippi Valley the king snake is greenish with white or yellow speckling. In Georgia, Alabama and Florida it is black or dark brown marked with yellow. The Californian subspecies is in two colour phases: one with yellow rings, the other with yellow stripes, the background colour of both being black or brown. These and other species and subspecies range over most of the United States northwards into southern Canada and southwards into Mexico. The milk snakes, up to $3\frac{1}{2}$ ft long, are closely related to the king snakes. Their name is sometimes applied to king snakes in different localities.

*Some king snakes are ringed red, yellow and black and look very like the venomous coral snakes. So they are sometimes called false coral snakes, a name also given to other colubrid snakes such as the rear-fanged **Erythrolamprus** of South America, red with black rings.*

Terrorising the rattlers

King snakes, active especially in afternoon and evening, do not pursue other snakes. They eat small mammals, usually rodents, as well as lizards and frogs, caught in meadows and wooded areas. Should one of them meet another snake, however, it will eat it. It strikes it with its teeth and grasps the neck of its victim, at the same time throwing its body round the other snake, killing it by suffocation, just as pythons and boas kill their prey. King snakes are immune to snake venom, even that of rattlesnakes and copperheads, and the danger they represent to other snakes is shown by the

behaviour of a rattlesnake in the presence of a king snake. Instead of coiling its body, raising its head to strike with its teeth, and raising its tail to shake its rattle, it keeps its head and neck on the ground and raises part of its body in a high loop, trying to beat off its attacker by blows from this loop.

The smaller milk snakes of North America take similar prey but the snakes they eat are younger and smaller. They are named for an alleged habit of taking milk from cows. This same story is current in parts of the world for other species of snakes. Not only is there no evidence to support it but the way a snake's teeth work make it virtually impossible to believe that any snake could take a cow's teat into its mouth without lacerating it badly.

Brighter babies

Mating takes place in spring, the female laying 10—30 white parchment-shelled eggs in summer. Sometimes these are laid on the ground, more usually they are under leaves and plant litter. In some species, she may coil her body around the eggs for the first day or so, but afterwards leaves them. They hatch in 4—6 weeks, the baby snakes being 7—8 in. long, coloured like the parents but with the colours brighter.

The long swallow

There are many stories, and photographs have appeared in the Press, of one snake swallowing another. This happens in zoos when two snakes seize the same food. Sooner or later their noses touch as they both try to swallow the same thing, and the one with the larger gape swallows the other. Doubtless this happens in the wild also, but rarely. There are, however, snakes like the European smooth snake *Coronella austriaca* which, besides eating frogs, lizards and mice, also eats snakes. One of the lizards it eats is the legless and snake-like slowworm,

Lampropeltis doliata amaura, Louisiana milk snake or 'false coral snake' as it is sometimes called.

John Tashjian at Fort Worth Zoo

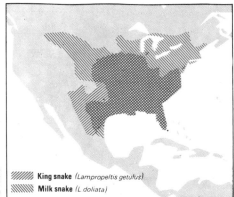

◁ *A snake is a snake to a snake-eating snake and the common king snake does not think twice about eating one of his own kind when he is hungry. In one rapid movement the king snake strikes the black snake, **Coluber**, and ties himself in a tight knot around its victim killing it by suffocation.*
▽ *Map showing the distribution of two species of **Lampropeltis.***
▽▽ *Freak of nature, a two-headed snake.*

▨▨▨ **King snake** (*Lampropeltis getulus*)	
▨▨▨ **Milk snake** (*L. doliata*)	

but smooth snakes, themselves only 18 in. long, will also eat young adders. Other snakes are snake-eaters to the extent of being famous for this habit, like the file snakes *Mehelya* of Africa. They behave like king snakes, in constricting their prey, and seem also to be immune to poison. The mussurana *Clelia clelia* of tropical America is another snake-eater. One mussurana (as stated, p 748) 6½ ft long that looked unduly swollen was found to have swallowed a 6ft fer-de-lance, the dreaded poisonous snake. The most famous snake-eater is perhaps the king cobra or hamadryad *Naja hannah*, of southeast Asia. It does not constrict its victims and it is not immune to poison, which is why it usually eats non-venomous snakes. It will, however, eat the other kind—including smaller king cobras.

Were it possible to know the truth we should doubtless find that many snake-eating snakes are cannibalistic, if only by accident. A snake is a snake to a snake-eating snake whatever its species. Even more bizarre things than this have been seen. FW Fitzsimons, the distinguished South African specialist in snakes, tells of a Cape file snake that intervened when two deadly night adders had each seized a leg of a frog. The file snake settled the argument by swallowing all three. Then there was Dudly-Duplex, the two-headed king snake of San Diego Zoo. One night one head tried to swallow the other. This was rescued the following morning. Later, the aggrieved head tried to take revenge—with fatal results for the two heads and the body to which they belonged.

class	**Reptilia**
order	**Squamata**
suborder	**Serpentes**
family	**Colubridae**
genus & species	***Lampropeltis getulus*** common *king snake* ***L. doliata*** *milk snake, others*

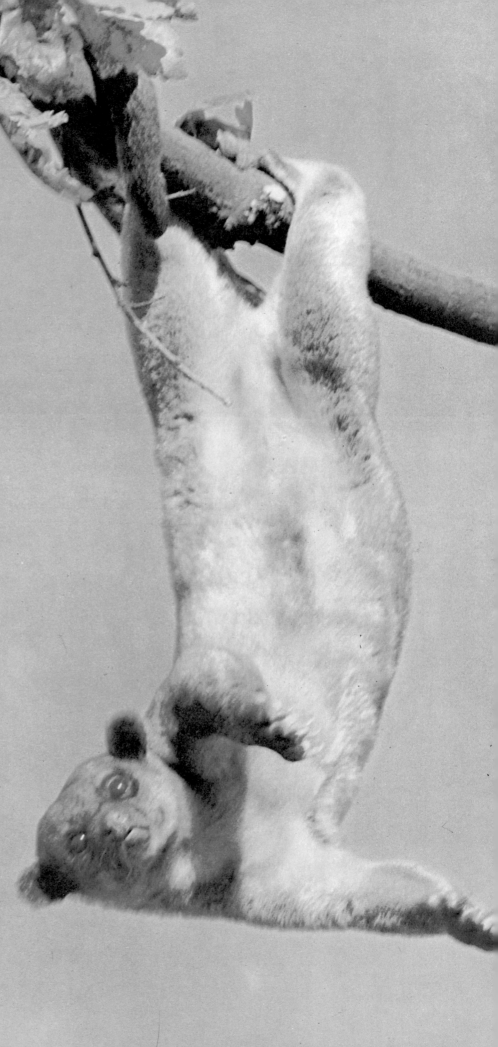

Kinkajou

This is one of many local names for a relative of the pandas living in tropical America, although it is likely to be called a honeybear when sold in pet shops. Another name used by South American Indians is potto, not to be confused with the primate living in Africa.

A kinkajou has a long body and short legs, with the forelegs shorter than the hindlegs. Its coat is of soft woolly fur, dark gold to brown with the underparts lighter. Its eyes are large, its ears small, and its tail is long. Each foot has five toes with short sharp claws. The usual size is 1 ft long in head and body with a 1½ft tail. The height at the shoulder is 10 in. and the weight up to 6 lb. The outstanding feature of this animal is that its tail is prehensile, like the tails of many South American monkeys. The Mexican name for a kinkajou is monkey lion, which aptly describes it.

Kinkajous range from southern Mexico through Central America and into South America at least as far south as the Matto Grosso in Brazil. Within much of this range, from Central America into northern South America lives a closely related and similar animal, the olingo. It is slightly smaller but with a longer, flattened and non-prehensile tail. Its fur is more golden and the tail is marked with dark rings. The fur on its face is paler than that on its body, and the olingo has been called the pale-faced kinkajou. Its habits are much like those of kinkajous and because they are apt to move about with parties of kinkajous they tend to be overlooked, so little is known about them. Indeed, olingos are sometimes sold as kinkajous.

Zool Soc London

The demon drink

One surprising feature about our information on the kinkajou is that although it is called the honeybear very few books say anything about it eating honey. The most complete account of its diet is in Lee S Crandall's *The Management of Wild Mammals in Captivity.* This lists the fruits, vegetables and bread it will eat, adds also raw or cooked meat, dog biscuit, cooked or raw egg, bone meal, cod-liver oil, condensed milk, ice cream—but no honey. In his *Living Mammals of the World,* Ivan T Sanderson says they gorge honey, lapping it up with their narrow 6in. tongues, from wild bees' nests. Most writers say the kinkajou is mild and docile, an affectionate pet, but one that can, if handled roughly, snarl and bite. Sanderson calls it a most dangerous pet because its honey-eating leads to an insatiable appetite for alcoholic liquors. He says that when inebriated a kinkajou goes quite mad, will attack its owner with tooth and claw, holding on with its tail and biting continually as no other animal will. Obviously, a kinkajou is a pet for the teetotal household only!

class	**Mammalia**
order	**Carnivora**
family	**Procyonidae**
genera & species	***Potos flavus*** kinkajou ***Bassaricyon gabbii*** olingo

◁ *Kinkajou climbing up his own tail while hanging from a keeper's hand. There are only two carnivores, the kinkajou and the unrelated binturong, with prehensile tails, which make a useful fifth limb for when the animal is climbing.* ▽ *Acrobat of the forest treetops.*

Important tailpiece

Kinkajous live in forests and spend all their time in the treetops, sleeping by day in hollows in the trunks, sometimes coming out on hot humid days to lie along a branch or in the tangle of a vine as in a hammock. At night they move about the trees singly, in pairs or in groups as when they converge on a single tree with a ripening crop of fruit. They move quickly and with agility through the trees, wrapping the tail around a branch for added support but they do not leap from branch to branch, as a monkey does. They move cautiously from one tree to another, making sure of the next foothold while anchoring themselves with the tail. Kinkajous are often kept in zoos and there a keeper will sometimes show how the animal will turn and climb up its own tail with the end of the tail wrapped round the keeper's arm. They bark if alarmed but otherwise their call is a shrill quavering scream.

A passion for fruit

Although a member of the Carnivora, or flesh-eaters, kinkajous live mainly on fruit. In captivity they readily eat oranges, apples, bananas and grapes, but will take bread, carrots and peanuts just as eagerly. With the softer fruits they scoop out the pulp with their mobile tongue, holding the fruit to the mouth with the forepaws. They also eat insects, and possibly small mammals and birds at times.

Long-lived in zoos

A number of kinkajou pairs have bred in zoos in Europe and America but nothing is known of their mating behaviour, the time of the breeding season or the gestation period. Usually there is one young at a birth, seldom two, but as many as four have been recorded. If correct, this larger number must be exceptional. The babies are born blind with a soft coat of black fur. They can hang by their tails at 7 weeks and their eyes open at 10 weeks. During the early days, judging from what has been seen in zoos, the mother leaves the baby in a hollow in a tree when she goes foraging, carrying it from one nest to another, if necessary, by holding it in her mouth by the scruff. Kinkajous are fairly long-lived, at least in zoos, the maximum age so far reported being 23 years 7 months.

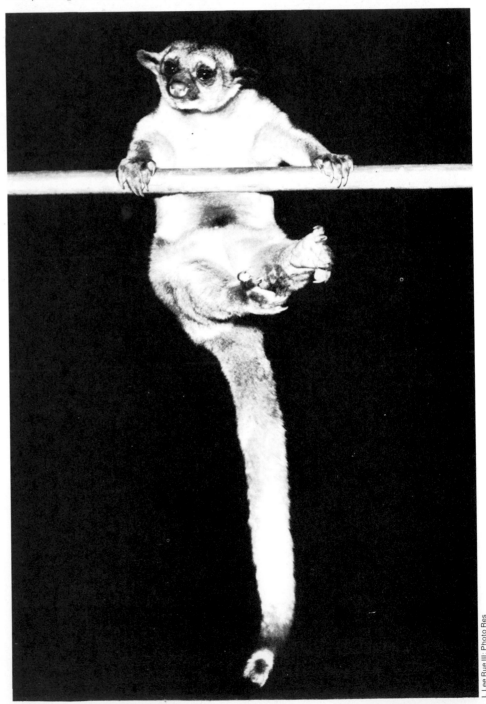
L Lee Rue III: Photo Res

Kissing gourami

This is a popular aquarium fish that has achieved fame for a single trick of behaviour that looks uncommonly like a familiar human action. Other than this the species would have remained in relative obscurity. 'Kissing' is by no means confined to this gourami, which is chosen here to show an interesting facet of animal behaviour.

There are several species of gouramis, all from southeast Asia, where they grow to a foot or more and are used for food. The kissing gourami may grow to a foot long, but when kept in an aquarium it is usually well short of this. Its body is flattened from side to side, oval in outline, with a pointed head ending in a pair of thickened lips. The greenish to grey-yellow dorsal and anal fins are long and prominent and both slope upwards from front to rear. The normal colour of the body is silvery green with dark stripes on the flanks but there is another colour phase, pinkish-white and somewhat iridescent.

Thick lips for breathing and eating

The kissing and other gouramis belong to the labyrinth fishes, which means they have an accessory breathing organ in the gills for taking in air at the surface, as well as breathing by gills. The kissing gourami not only rises to the surface from time to time to gulp air, and therefore can live in water that is slightly fouled, but it also feeds at the surface. The thickened lips probably have an advantage in these two respects. The food consists of both animal and plant matter and in an aquarium kissing gouramis eat dried shrimps and powdered oatmeal, water fleas and dried spinach. To some extent they will feed on the small algae that grow on the sides of the aquarium.

Life history little known

There is still some doubt about their breeding habits. Many labyrinth fishes build bubble nests for their eggs but so far as we know kissing gouramis build no nest but lay 400—2 000 floating eggs. They seem to ignore these as well as the young which hatch in 24 hours. The baby fishes eat ciliated protistans for their first week, taking water fleas after this, graduating to the mixed diet as they grow older. They begin to breed when 3—5 in. long.

Mystery of the kiss

Nobody seems very clear whether this is an aggressive action or part of the courtship. Probably it enters into both. When several kissing gouramis are kept together in one aquarium the larger of them bother the smaller by 'sucking' at their flanks. They will do the same with fishes of other species. This is probably aggressive. When a pair are together, however, they can be seen to face each other, swaying backwards and forwards, as if hung on invisible threads, and then they come together, mouth to mouth, their thick lips firmly placed together in an exaggerated kissing action. Like other labyrinth fishes the male wraps himself around the body of the female when mating. This is preceded by the two swimming round and round each other in a circling movement, after which they again come together, lips to lips, in a seeming kiss.

A touching scene — like mirror images of each other two gouramis 'kiss'. It is not fully understood why this fish, a favourite among tropical fish fanciers, makes this familiar human action. It may be one of aggression or, as we tend to think, a sign of affection.

Paying lip-service

The use of the mouth as a test of strength in fighting is common among the higher animals. It is frequently seen in aquarium fishes, especially among cichlids and labyrinth fishes. One fish butting another with its mouth is often used in courtship, especially by the smaller freshwater fishes, and it seems likely that the mouth-wrestling and the butting lead on to the kissing. At all events, A van der Nieuwenhuizen, in his book *Tropical Aquarium Fish*, takes the view that in the cichlid, known as the blue acara *Aequidens latifrons*, mouth-wrestling is used to defeat a rival as well as court a mate. He maintains that when a pair indulge in a bout of mouth-wrestling which ends in stalemate this means the two are physically and psychologically suited and the chances of their breeding are high. The mouth-tugging, as he calls it, may last for hours and be repeated day after day, to end in a genuine lovers' choice. The chances are that the kissing of the gourami has exactly the same importance, so it is a true lovers' kiss.

class	**Pisces**
order	**Perciformes**
family	**Anabantidae**
genus & species	***Helostoma temmincki***

Kite

The kite is a bird of prey, whose smooth gliding flight has given its name to man-made flying devices. It belongs to a sub-family Milvinae of the falcon family. The subfamily also includes several fish eagles and the Everglade kite (p 727) but attention is given here mainly to the true kites, genus **Milvus.** These have long pointed wings angled at the wrists and a forked tail.

Both sexes of the kite (sometimes called the red kite) are 2 ft long. Their back and wings are dark brown with lighter borders to the feathers, the underparts are rusty red with dark streaks and the head is greyish, nearly white in old birds, with dark streaks. In flight they show a con-spicuous white patch under each wing. Black kites are slightly smaller, darker and their tails are less forked.

The range of the kite includes most of Europe except the extreme north, much of France, the Low Countries and northern Italy. It also includes Asia Minor, the coastal strip of northwest Africa, the Canaries and the Cape Verde Islands. The black kite ranges over Europe and Asia except for the extreme north, Africa except for the Sahara and much of Australia.

A number of other Milvinae have been called kites, the most famous being the Brahminy kite **Maliastur indus**, ranging from India to the Solomon Islands and Australia. This is the sacred kite of India, 18 in. long, living in the swamps and feeding on frogs and carrion. It is brown with a white head and shoulders.

There is another subfamily, of black-shouldered kites, sometimes called white-tailed kites, which somewhat resembles the true kites but differs in habits. Species are found in America, Africa, Southern Asia and Australia. Typical of these is **Elanus caeruleus** of Africa. It is grey and white with black markings on the fore edge of the wing. The African black-shouldered kite feeds mainly at dusk and dawn, quartering the ground at low level.

Masters of soaring flight

The kite lives in wooded river valleys, but it is sometimes seen in broad-leaved forests, most often at their fringes. It may spend long periods perched on a branch, always alert, descending to the ground when it sees food. On the ground it is quite active, hopping rather than walking, and having found food the kite usually returns to a perch to eat it. In the air kites appear more buoyant than buzzards as they drift high over the valleys or soar, glide and occasion-ally hover on wings more slender than those of the buzzard. When looked at from above, the tail is noticeably red.

No food refused

The kite has a justified reputation for being a scavenger, and will take any dead animal food lying around, including garbage. It

Popperfoto

△ *Black-winged or white-tailed kite* **Elanus caeruleus** *can hover like a kestrel.*

▽ *Yellow-billed kite* **Milvus aegypticus** *wheels at no great height searching for food.*

will, however, take any small mammals, from rabbits and squirrels to mice, any birds —especially young ones—and older birds that are injured, as well as frogs, lizards, snakes and insects. Grasshoppers especially are picked up on the ground and beetles are taken on the wing. Dead fish and fish offal are eaten and in the Canaries and the Cape Verde Islands kites are familiar in ports and fish markets.

Garbage-filled nests
As with all large birds of prey, courtship is marked by soaring flights and a mewing call. Kites are said to pair for life and about March—earlier in the southerly parts of their range—each pair begins to court in earnest, sailing at great heights, circling around each other or gliding low over the treetops. Sometimes one of them will fly low with a stick or wisp of wool in its talons, the other will follow and the 'plaything' will be passed from one to the other, usually ending up in the nest. The nest is a platform of sticks consolidated with earth, close to the main trunk of a tall slender oak or pine. It is lined with wool, moss and an assortment of rubbish, such as hair, paper, rag, grass, dung, bones and fur. The 2–3 white eggs, lightly marked with brown, are laid in mid-April and incubated by only the female for about a month, the male bringing food to her. He continues to do this for a while after the eggs have hatched and then the female joins him in hunting, both bringing food to the fledglings until they are 2 months old.

Black and red compared
The black kite has a similar history except that it tends to live more consistently near rivers and takes a higher proportion of fish carrion. It will also catch large fish swimming at the surface in rivers. In Africa it is noted for preying on swarming locusts or hunting for insects driven out by grass fires. Some red and the black kites migrate, mainly from the northern parts of the range to more southerly latitudes with the approach of winter. The red kite, however, does not move farther south than the Mediterranean region whereas the black kite tends to winter in tropical Africa.

Decline of the kite
In the Middle Ages kites, probably both the red and the black, were numerous in Britain but today only a few pairs of red kites survive, almost confined to Wales, and only five black kites have been seen in the British Isles in the last century. Richard Fitter recalls, in his *London's Natural History,* that the secretary to Baron Leo von Rozmital, visiting London from Bohemia in 1465, noted that nowhere had he seen so many kites as on London Bridge. Charles Clusius, the Flemish botanist, visiting England in 1571, thought there were as many kites in England as in Cairo. They were then protected birds and so tame they would come down for carrion and garbage among crowds of people, or snatch 'bread smeared with butter, in the Flemish fashion, given to them by their mothers from the hands of children'. European soldiers serving in the Middle East have often had similar experiences when eating their rations. By the 18th century kites were rare in Britain, being no longer protected. The last pair nested in Hyde Park in 1777 and the last one seen flying over London was June 24, 1859—over Piccadilly!

Although the list of items of food taken is a long one, kites tend to have different preferences in different districts. Some undoubtedly make a practice of taking chicks and ducklings from farmyards and this almost certainly led to their persecution. People's habits changed, also, and there was less garbage about in London and elsewhere by the 18th century. By 1905 only five red kites were known in Britain, in mid-Wales. By 1910 these had increased to 10 pairs, but by 1938 there were only 15 kites in Britain. Some protective measures were attempted during this period but records were not well kept. In 1949 the West Wales Field Society set up its Kite Field Committee. By persuading farmers on whose land the kites nested to leave them alone and by trying—not always successfully —to keep people away from the nesting areas, the kite has been given protection ever since. The position in 1968 was that there were 24 or 25 pairs, 20 of which nested, and 12 young birds were reared.

△ *A pair of red kites merge well with the pine tree as they guard their nest.*

▽ *Reputation for scavenging—a black kite stands over the carcase of a red deer.*

Bel Vienne. Jacana

Eric Hosking

class	**Aves**
order	**Falconiformes**
family	**Accipitridae**
genus & species	***Milvus migrans*** *black kite* ***M. milvus*** *red kite*

Kittiwake

The kittiwake is a small gull that differs from other gulls in frequenting open water rather than shores, and in nesting on cliff ledges. It is small, about 16 in. long, and looks like a common gull, but has no white tips to the black edges of its wings. The body is white with grey wings and back, but in winter the grey extends up the neck to the crown. The bill is yellow and the legs black. Young kittiwakes have a black band across the back of the neck and another across the wings.

Kittiwakes live in the North Atlantic Ocean, breeding as far south as Brittany and Newfoundland. To the north, they breed in Spitzbergen, Franz Josef Land and Severnaya Zemlya. A second species, the red-legged kittiwake, breeds in the Bering Sea and North Pacific as far south as the Kurile and Aleutian Islands.

Fritz Siedel

J Allan Cash

Head for heights

◁◁ *Sheer drop to the sea below—the kittiwake must have a head for heights to lead its precarious life. Kittiwakes nest in large colonies on the narrowest of cliff ledges.*

◁ *Each kittiwake, out of necessity, builds a solid nest of mud, grass or seaweed, so preventing the eggs from toppling over the edge of the cliff. Even when the chicks have hatched they are unable to run about but must stay in the nest for the first few weeks.*

△ *A kittiwake emerges from a plunge dive. It feeds on fish, molluscs and plankton and does not steal eggs and young birds as do other gulls.*

Oceanic seabird

Outside the breeding season kittiwakes spend their time at sea in flocks of 1 000 or more. They can be found on the pack ice of the Arctic Sea, provided there is enough open water for feeding, and have been found within 130 miles of the North Pole. Kittiwakes are rarely seen inland, usually only after a storm. Sometimes a flock is caught by a storm and driven into the shore and inland where many may die. There is a general southward movement in the autumn after the breeding season, returning the following spring. There is also a movement around the oceans; kittiwakes ringed off the British Isles have been recovered in Newfoundland, Labrador and Greenland.

Food is mainly plankton

Kittiwakes are found in the plankton-rich surface waters of the ocean. They usually feed by plunge-diving—diving with wings half-folded but not completely submerging. They do, however, sometimes submerge completely and swim underwater with their wings. They catch a variety of floating animals such as crustaceans, squids, worms and fishes. Occasionally freshwater or shore creatures are taken and there is even one record of a pigmy shrew being taken. Kittiwakes are not usually attracted to carrion and offal like other gulls but will sometimes follow fishing boats and frequent canning factories to feed on the scraps.

Kittiwakes have been reported as attacking grey seals that were carrying fish in their mouths, settling or hovering near their heads and lunging at them.

Nesting on cliffs

Towards the end of May or June, kittiwakes appear around the coasts where they nest in large colonies, sometimes of up to 100 000 pairs. They often nest on the same cliffs as guillemots, fulmars and shags. Occasionally they build on inland cliffs or on windowsills, which are man-made equivalents of rock ledges, and some kittiwake colonies are on rocky islets. There may be competition for nest sites and the kittiwakes nest on the narrowest ledges, to which the pair cling, facing inwards, during courtship. The two kittiwakes bow and rub each other's bills and heads, or face each other and utter their characteristic calls of 'kitt-i-waak', at the same time showing the orange inside of their mouths.

Most gulls build very scanty nests, making little more than a depression in the ground with a lining of grass and other plants. Kittiwakes, on the other hand, build a solid nest of mud, grass or seaweed, forming the cup needed to keep eggs from falling off a narrow, often uneven ledge. The collection of nest material is a community event. Several dozen kittiwakes fly inland and settle on a piece of boggy ground or other suitable place where they can pick up beakfuls of mud and grass and fly 'kitt-i-waaking' back to the cliffs. The nest material is placed on the ledge, trampled down, and finally a lining of dry grass is added. Not all the material is collected on these communal expeditions; kittiwakes regularly steal material from their neighbours' nests.

Both parents incubate the 2 eggs for 3 weeks. Unlike other gulls, the chicks are unable to run about and have to spend their first few weeks in the nest. This means that they cannot practise flying so vigorously as do other young seabirds, or run away if attacked by their nestmates or by adult kittiwakes. If they are attacked they hide their heads in submission, thereby reducing the aggression of their attackers.

Cliff safety first

Gulls that nest on open ground often fall prey to predators such as foxes or stoats, but by nesting on inaccessible cliffs kittiwakes are safe from such attacks. It is thought that this habit has occurred through natural selection and much of their breeding habits have altered to fit the new way of life. In the course of a study on the habits of kittiwakes, Esther Cullen made a list of the changes that distinguish kittiwakes from the gulls that nest on open ground. Because of the safety of the cliffs kittiwakes rarely give alarm calls and stay on their nests until one comes quite close. Unlike the chicks of other gulls, kittiwake chicks are not camouflaged and the parents do not remove eggshells or droppings from the nest to make it less conspicuous. They do, however, swallow or throw away waste food as a sanitary measure. Other gulls do not do this but they can lead their chicks away from the nest before feeding them. At the start of the breeding season most gulls are wary of their nesting ground because of the dangers of predation and pairing takes place away from the nesting ground. Kittiwakes, on the other hand, mate on their nests.

Some changes have been necessary to live on cliff ledges. A solid nest is needed for the safety of eggs and chicks and sharp claws and strong toes for hanging on. The violent, wing-beating battles other gulls indulge in are impossible on a narrow ledge and kittiwakes fight by grabbing and twisting each other's bills. The chicks feed by taking food from the parents' throats. If they were fed by the parent regurgitating food onto the ground for them to peck, the food might be lost over the edge.

class	**Aves**
order	**Charadriiformes**
family	**Laridae**
genus & species	***Rissa tridactyla*** kittiwake ***R. brevirostris*** *red-legged kittiwake*

Kittiwakes quarrelling over food in mid-air: a rare photograph of unusual behaviour (by G Rüppell).

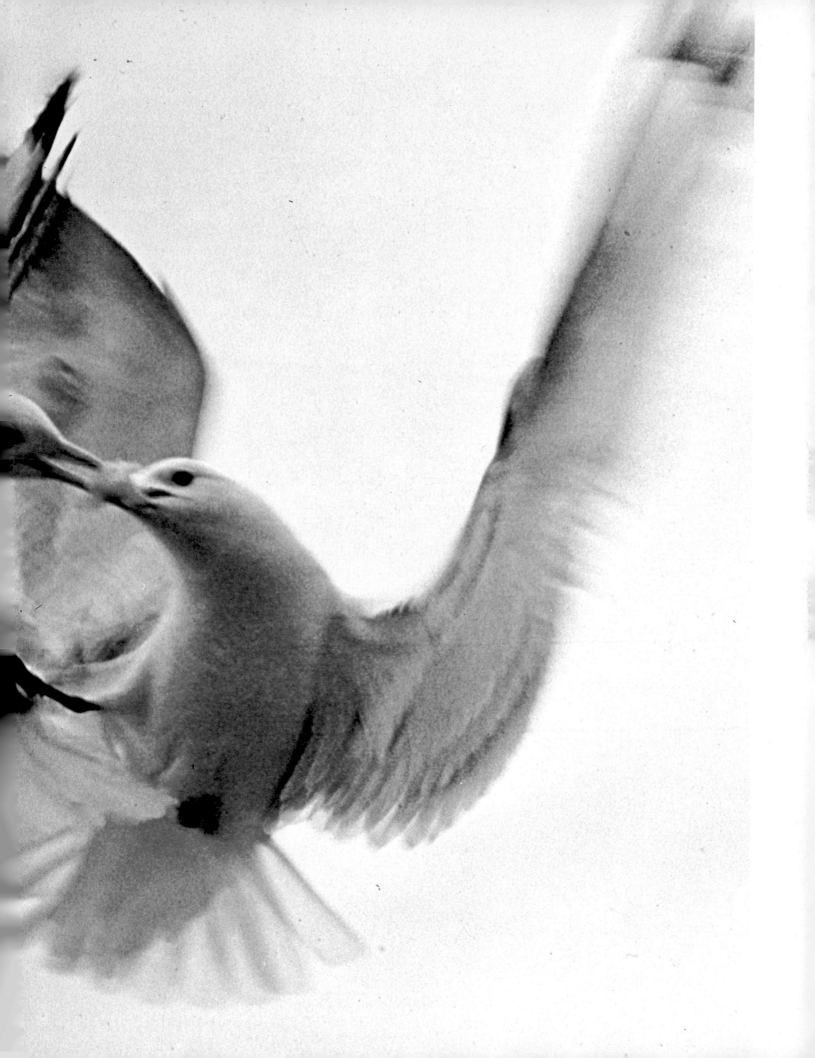

Kiwi

The kiwi is the smallest flightless running bird in the southern hemisphere, the other runners being the emu, cassowary, ostrich and rhea. There are three species in New Zealand, each about the size of a domestic fowl, with a rounded body, no tail, stout but short legs, strong claws on their three toes and a long slender bill with slit-like nostrils at its tip. They range in size from a bantam to an Orpington and in weight from 3 – 9 lb, the females being larger than the males. The wings are very small, 2 in. long, and completely hidden by the hair-like body feathers that make up the plumage. The eyes are small but there are many long bristles at the base of the bill which are probably used as organs of touch. The ears are large and are the chief sensory organs used in detecting danger.

Kiwis are so different anatomically from the other running birds that they are probably only distantly related to them. They are more closely related to the extinct moas of New Zealand.

Waddling nightbird

The home of the kiwi is in the kauri pine forests with their tree ferns and swampy ground. Here they spend the day in burrows or under buttress roots of large trees. They are shy, retiring and hard to see in the forest because of the gloom and the birds' dark brown colouring. They come out at night and waddle along, their legs being set well apart. Their run is a long-striding waddle, with the bill held well out in front.

Food for all seasons

When feeding a kiwi moves quietly, probably feeling its way to a large extent with the bill bristles. At the slightest alarm it dashes rapidly to cover. Its main food, when the ground is moist, is earthworms and insects and their larvae. The tip of the long bill overlaps the lower half, so the bill can be thrust deep in the ground, driven by the short, thick neck. The bird tracks its prey mainly by smell. When the ground is dry in summer, the kiwi picks up fallen forest fruits and eats a large number of leaves.

Testing its sense of smell

It has always been assumed that the kiwi finds its food by smell, although most birds have a weak sense of smell. In December 1968, Bernice M Wenzel, of the University of California, published an account in *Nature* (Vol 220, p 1133) of a series of experiments carried out in New Zealand. Sets of tapering aluminium tubes were sunk into the ground in two kiwi aviaries. The tests, repeated over a period of 3 months, consisted of placing food in one tube, earth in another and a strong odorant in a third. By ringing the changes, such as using different odorants and different ways of masking the contents of the various tubes, it was proved beyond doubt that a kiwi can smell food several inches down in a way that no other bird is able to do.

Unusually large eggs

Although kiwis' nests have often been found, not much is known about the breeding or nesting habits. The nest is made in a hollow log or among the roots of a large tree. Sometimes it is in a hole or burrow in a soft bank, enlarged by the bird itself. Kiwis lay 1 or 2 very large chalky-white eggs, each about 5 in. long, weighing about a pound. This is $\frac{1}{8}$ of the hen kiwi's body weight, not $\frac{1}{4}$ as is sometimes stated. The male, as is usual with running birds, does the incubating, which lasts for 75 – 80 days. The chicks are small balls of soft hair-like feathers with a spindly beak. They remain in the nest for 6 days after hatching, receiving no food during this time. Then they follow their parents on their nightly forays, finding their own food, after the male has helped by clearing the ground for them. The normal call of the male is thin and reedy; that of the female is more hoarse. It is a two-note call, made only at night, and sounds like 'k-wee', with the accent on the second part.

At Hawke's Bay a colony of kiwis is kept under protection. Nesting boxes are provided and there it was noticed that during the incubation period the hen tapped at intervals on the box and the male inside tapped back. This may be a means of communication between the two partners.

From pot to popularity

The kiwi population has decreased over the past century. They were prized by the Maoris as a delicacy, and their feathers were woven into cloaks for the chieftains. Then the early settlers hunted them for food. The birds also suffered from dogs, cats, stoats, weasels and other introduced animals. Their habitat has been reduced through the country being opened up for agriculture. In contrast with their falling numbers, their popularity has increased. Their image is seen on postage stamps and coins and on the trademarks of many products from shoe polish to textiles. The name became most familiar to people in Britain and in other parts of the world during the First World War because the New Zealand troops were called Kiwis. The Royal Air Force also perpetuated the name to some extent when its non-flying members were nicknamed Kiwis.

class	**Aves**
order	**Apterygiformes**
family	**Apterygidae**
genus & species	***Apteryx australis*** common or brown kiwi ***A. haasti*** great spotted or large grey kiwi ***A. oweni*** little spotted or little grey kiwi

Earthworm forager afield: the flightless kiwi of New Zealand, with beak outstretched, walks through undergrowth in long-striding waddles.

MF Soper

Klipspringer

The klipspringer is a small antelope related to dik-diks which is adapted, like the chamois in the northern hemisphere, to life on bare and inaccessible rocky places. The klipspringer is 3 ft long in head and body with 2–4 in. of tail and stands up to 22 in. at the shoulder. It weighs up to 40 lb. The thick, wavy coat is yellowish to reddish, with yellowish white or white on the underparts and the insides of the legs. Each hair of the upper parts is minutely banded with yellow and black, giving a pepper-and-salt effect. The hairs are bristle-like, stout and with an inner pith quite unlike those of any other antelope.

*The head is broad and triangular with a pointed snout but broad mouth, the muzzle being bare and the nostrils small. The ears are large and rounded, and their inner faces are conspicuously ridged, suggesting efficient hearing because ridges of this kind have been shown to direct sound waves more effectively on to the eardrum. There is a prominent bare opening to the scent glands on the face, in front of each eye, but there are no foot glands. The legs are stout and each ends in a hairy pastern, with black hair, and two cylindrical hoofs, each hoof 1 in. high and the same across, blunted at their tips and with their bases high from the ground when the animal is in motion. The horns are short, straight spikes ringed at the base and usually worn by males only but there is one race in the Tanganyika area (**schillingi**) in which the females often have horns.*

A dozen races have been recognized from Northern Nigeria to the Sudan, Ethiopia and Somalia, south to the Cape.

Splendid jumpers

Klipspringers live in cliff ravines, on high rocky prominences and rocky kopjes, and in the bush surrounding them, where they feed. Traces of them have been found on Mt Elgon in Kenya up to 14 800 ft. They are solitary or form small groups of up to eight. Once disturbed they make off for the rocks or, if already on the rocks, they stand with all four feet together, alert, rigid and hard to see. When not unduly disturbed and if only their curiosity is aroused they give a shrill whistle. On further alarm they retreat, always uphill and on reaching the summit, a klipspringer pauses for a last look backwards before disappearing. The alarm call is a curious discordant squeaking. The name, which is Afrikaans for rock jumper, is from the animal's amazing capacity for jumping from crag to crag. It is a terrific jumper, more surefooted than any goat, bouncing up an almost perpendicular cliff like a rubber ball or dropping down a precipitous face without losing foothold. FW Fitzsimon, the South African naturalist, observed one leap 30 ft from the edge of a rocky precipice to a jutting ledge below, steady itself for a moment, then run at a fast pace obliquely down the precipice.

Delicately poised: the klipspringer is renowned for its ability to scale seemingly inaccessible rocky places. It has been claimed that it can land on a point no bigger than a penny!

South African Tourist Corporation

A bare living

Its food is leaves and grass or, if in a habitat with little or no bush around, rock plants, especially succulents. Astley Maberly maintains that it must get its moisture from dew or small quantities of water caught in holes in the rocks, as it does not visit waterholes.

Statuesque buck

The breeding season is probably extended over a long period, the single young being born between September and the end of January. The gestation period is 214 days. A feature of the rut seems to be for the buck to stand on watch on a pinnacle of rock with the hoofs all close together.

Odds against survival

The probable enemies are leopards, large birds of prey and pythons. The only protection is the almost moss-like coat of brittle hair which comes away in tufts and seems at times to nonplus the enemy. The lost hair is soon replaced by a new growth. At one time when klipspringers were more numerous, they were hunted for this hair which was springy and light enough to be used for stuffing saddles and mattresses. Astley Maberly is of the opinion that the klipspringer's coat serves as a cushion against rocks, or against thorns as the animal scrapes past them. On precipitous slopes it could not afford to have its coat caught even for a moment in a thorn tuft growing among rocks or in a crevice in a rock face. The real long-term danger to the species is that, owing to its special requirements, it is unable to adapt to changes, which often lead to local extinction. At the present time klipspringers still survive in fair numbers in some places but should extinction ever be threatened it is unlikely the species could be preserved in captivity. The animals are not often seen in zoos although one lived for 15 years in the St Louis Zoological Park, in the United States. The experience there, however, where there has been the greatest success in keeping klipspringers, is not very promising. A number of young were reared from a small group of these animals obtained in 1935 and a considerable stock was built up. Then, when success seemed assured, the vitality seemed to wane and the herd 'disintegrated'. A tall kiosk of rough stone was built to resemble their natural habitat but they made less use of this than was hoped and this may have had something to do with their deterioration.

Point of balance

The klipspringer is always figured standing on a pinnacle of rock with all four feet close together, the animal balanced on its 'points'. It has been claimed that it can spring from the ground to land on such a pinnacle no bigger at the top than a penny, which is just over 1 in. diameter. If true it shows remarkable judgement, balance and poise. It may be that the story improves with the telling because the account varies with the writer from a penny to a silver dollar or 'several inches'. Even so, there is an implied skill which compels comparison with a ballet dancer poised on the points of her shoes which are shaped not unlike the hoofs of the klipspringer—and the animal's life depends on their unerring accuracy.

class	**Mammalia**
order	**Artiodactyla**
family	**Bovidae**
genus & species	***Oreotragus oreotragus***

*Aptly named: South American apteronotid knife-fish **Sternopygus macrurus** moves backwards and forwards by undulating its long anal fin.*

Knife-fish

For a fish to be called a knife-fish its body must be broad and thin. The knife-fish of tropical Africa and southern and southeast Asia, belonging to the family Notopteridae, is very much flattened from side to side and the blade-like body ends in what is almost a point. One member of this family has already been dealt with under feather-back (p 741). There are three other families of knife-fishes, living in South America, and they belong to a different order. They are the Gymnotidae, Apteronotidae and Rhamphichthyidae. Together they give us an excellent example of convergent evolution, in which two or more unrelated animals have come to look alike. The last three families are related to carp (order Cypriniformes), the Notopteridae being nearer to the arapaima (order Osteoglossidae).

Knife-fishes are often kept in aquaria and anyone wishing to air his knowledge—or, conversely, not wishing to expose his ignorance—needs to take a second look to know whether the particular fish he is looking at is from South America or from tropical Africa and Asia. Knife-fishes are separated into families on the basis of their anatomy, and one thing that helps us tell straight away whether a knife-fish in the aquarium before us comes from the Old World or the New World is that the South American knife-fishes have a well-marked tentacle lying in front of each nostril.

Forward and backward swimmers

In all knife-fishes, the abdominal cavity and digestive organs occupy a small part of the body behind the head so the vent is well forward, where the pectoral fins would be in an ordinary fish. All the fins are small, even the tail fin, and only one is prominent: the anal fin, which runs from behind the vent along the underside of the body, and is continuous, or nearly so, with the very small tail fin. Knife-fishes, from wherever they come, swim by wave-like movements of the anal fin. When the flow is reversed the fish moves backward with equal ease. This is swimming reduced to a simple formula. With the body held rigid the knife-fish moves forward or backward, using only one fin, the long anal fin.

Two ways of breathing

All knife-fishes live in quiet weedy waters, in the side reaches of large rivers or in stagnant backwaters. In an aquarium they do best when shaded or given dimly lit places into which they can retire. They need to come to the surface to gulp air. In the South American knife-fishes the swimbladder has been transformed into a kind of lung. In the knife-fishes of the Old World, at least in the species studied, air is gulped into the gill cavity and the spent air is later given out through the stomach, intestine and vent. All knife-fishes feed at night or in twilight, on animal and plant food. In aquaria they are fed with chopped meat, worms and rolled oats, as well as small invertebrates such as water fleas, insect larvae and small fishes, although little is known for certain about what they eat in their native habitats. There is no way of telling male from female and little is known about their breeding.

Groping in the dark

The Nile fish, with similar movements and shape to knife-fishes, is a species that has been intensively studied because of the special use it makes of electric organs. It is of interest to note that the South American knife-fishes also generate electricity, from organs derived from outer parts of trunk and tail muscles. These generate impulses at frequencies between 1 and 1 000 per second. Some species produce 1—5 pulses per second while resting, increasing this to 20 per second when excited. Others produce up to 1 000 pulses per second. These electrical pulses set currents flowing in the water around the fish, the pattern of the current being altered by objects in the surrounding water. Animals have a higher conductivity than water, rocks have a lower conductivity. An animal concentrates the current so increasing the current flowing through nearby parts of the knife-fish's body. A rock has the reverse effect. So the fish can tell animal from mineral, food from an obstacle—but the current is not strong enough to kill prey.

class	**Pisces**
order	**Osteoglossiformes**
family	**Notopteridae**
genera	***Notopterus, Xenomystis***
order	**Cypriniformes**
families	**Gymnotidae, Apteronotidae, Rhamphichthyidae**
genera	***Gymnotus, Sternarchus, Hypopomus***, *others*

*False feather **Xenomystis nigri**. Its sole claim to generic recognition is the fact that it lacks the dorsal fin common to the rest of the family.*

Made-to-measure: with no eucalyptus tree available a koala seems to enjoy a change squatting up a telegraph pole on Phillip Island, off eastern Australia.

Graham Pizzey

Koala

The koala is probably Australia's favourite animal. It is known affectionately as the Australian teddy bear although there are a dozen names to choose from. At various times it has been called bangaroo, koolewong, narnagoon, buidelbeer, native bear, karbor, cullawine, colo, koala wombat and New Holland sloth! The last two have an especial interest. For a long time it was believed the koala was most nearly related to the wombat and was placed in a family on its own, the Phascolarctidae, near that of the wombat. Now it is placed in the Phalangeridae with the opossums. In habits the koala recalls the slow loris

and the sloth, two very different animals which also move in a lethargic way.

The koala is like a small bear, 2 ft high, up to 33 lb weight, with tufted ears, small eyes with a vertical slit pupil and a prominent beak-like snout. Tailless except for a very short rounded stump, it has a thick ash-grey fur with a tinge of brown on the upper parts, yellowish white on the hindquarters and white on the under parts. It has cheek pouches for storing food and the brood pouch of the female opens backwards. All four feet are grasping. On the front feet the first two of the five toes are opposed to the rest and the first toe on the hindfoot is opposed. Also on the hindfoot the second and third toes are joined in a common skin.

Ace tree-climbers

The koala is essentially tree-living, only occasionally descending to lick earth— apparently to aid digestion—or to shuffle slowly to another tree. If forced to the ground its main concern is to reach another tree and climb it, scrambling up even smooth trunks to the swaying topmost branches where it clings with the powerful grip of all four feet. Although its legs are short they are strong and there are sharp claws on the toes. When climbing a trunk its forelegs reach out at an angle of 45° while the hindlegs are directly under the body. It climbs in a series of jumps of 4–5 in. at a time. During the day it sleeps curled up in a tree-fork. It never enters hollows in trees. Koalas are inoffensive although they have harsh grating voices, said to be like a hand-saw cutting through a thin board; it has been

1215

claimed that they have the loudest Australian voice, other than the flying phalanger.

Fussy feeders

At night the koala climbs to the topmost branches to find its only food: the tender shoots of eucalyptus, 12 species of which are eaten. A koala is said to smell strongly of eucalyptus. Bernhard Grzimek has spoken of koalas as smelling like cough lozenges. Their feeding is, however, more restricted than this. Different races of koala eat only certain species of gum tree. Koalas on the east coast of Australia feed only on the spotted gum and the tallow wood, in Victoria only the red gum. Even then they cannot use all the leaves on a chosen gum. At certain times the older leaves, sometimes the young leaves at the tips of the branches, release prussic acid—a deadly poison—when chewed. So, as more and more gum trees have been felled, koalas have become increasingly hemmed in, prisoners of their specialised diet. One of the difficulties of saving the koala by having special reserves is to supply enough trees for them of the right kind. Koalas are said to eat mistletoe and box leaves as well, and a koala in captivity was persuaded to eat bread and milk, but without gum leaves they cannot survive.

Get off my back!

Another drawback to preserving the koala is that it is a slow breeder. Usually the animal is solitary or lives in small groups. At breeding time a boss male forms a small harem which he guards. The gestation period is 25—35 days and there is normally only one young at a birth, $\frac{3}{4}$ in. long and $\frac{1}{5}$ oz weight. It is fully furred at 6 months but continues to stay with the mother for another 6 months after leaving the pouch, riding pick-a-back on her, which has led to many endearing photographs. On weaning it obtains nourishment by eating partially digested food that has passed through the mother's digestive tract. The young koala is sexually mature at 4 years, and the longest lived koala was 20 years old when it died.

Pitiless persecution

Until less than a century ago there were millions of koalas, especially in eastern Australia. Now they are numbered in thousands. In 1887—89 and again in 1900—1903 epidemics swept through them, killing large numbers. This was at a time when it was a favourite 'sport' to shoot these sitting targets, often taking several shots to finish one animal which meanwhile cried piteously, like a human baby, a fact that caused Australian naturalists to condemn the sport as the most callous. At all times koalas are a prey to forest fires as well as to land clearance for human settlement. Moreover a market was developed for their pelts, their fur being thick and able to withstand hard usage. In 1908 nearly 58 000 koala pelts were marketed in Sydney alone. In 1920—21 a total of 205 679 were marketed and in 1924 over two million were exported. By this time public opinion was being aroused and before long efforts were being made to protect the surviving populations and to establish sanctuaries for them and ensure their future.

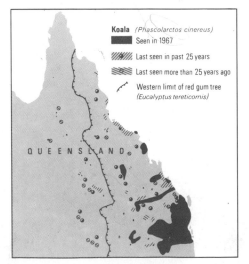

Koala (Phascolarctos cinereus)

■ Seen in 1967

▨ Last seen in past 25 years

▧ Last seen more than 25 years ago

⌐ Western limit of red gum tree (Eucalyptus tereticornis)

QUEENSLAND

Curious cuddly: favourite of millions, the koala is the Australian teddy bear. It spends most of its time shuffling about its eucalyptus tree-top home. The baby above has climbed onto its mother's back from a downward opening pouch. At a year (right) it is about to leave its mother and find its own gum tree.
Numbers have seriously decreased in the last 100 years mainly due to fires destroying their gum trees and from persecution by man. From a 1967 survey in Queensland the present-day distribution was established in that state (left).

class	**Mammalia**
order	**Marsupialia**
family	**Phalangeridae**
genus & species	***Phascolarctos cinereus***

Kob

Kob are antelopes, near relatives of water-buck from which they differ in their short coat, lack of a mane, short lyre-shaped horns and well-developed face glands, one in front of each eye. They also have scent glands in the groin (inguinal glands). The lechwe, another close relative, has more lyre-shaped horns with a double curve, no face glands and only rudimentary inguinal glands. Only the males, in all three, have horns.

The two species of kob are the true kob and the puku. The first, which includes two subspecies, the Uganda and the white-eared kob, ranges from Guinea to Uganda. The buck stands 3 ft at the shoulder and weighs 200 lb, the doe being smaller and weighing 145 lb. The coat varies across the range from orange or red to blackish-brown with white round the eyes and at the bases of the ears. The fronts of the forelegs are black, often with a white hoof-band, and the muzzle, lips, underparts and insides of the thighs are white. The puku, found in Zambia and part of Malawi, is 2—3 in. shorter at the shoulder, the buck weighing up to 170 lb, the doe up to 140 lb. The coloration of the puku differs only in details: no black on the legs, no white hoof-band, and the white eye-ring is narrower. The coat is longer and rougher.

Herds within herds

Kob are animals with a complicated social order. Looking over the African savannah we see a large herd of kob scattered unevenly. In one place we see a few hundred and a few miles away there is another concentration of them. It all seems to be haphazard but when Dr Hal Buechner, of the Smithsonian Institution in Washington, made his now famous studies less than 20 years ago, he found there was order in this apparent confusion.

On closer inspection, a herd of kob is seen to be made up of several groups and some solitary animals, grazing or resting and chewing the cud. A few will be moving about restlessly, but never straying over an invisible boundary line enclosing the territory of the herd. There were 15 000 kob in the Toro Game Reserve when Buechner came to study them. They were spread over 158 square miles and within this area there were 13 breeding grounds. Each ground was on a ridge or a knoll with good grazing, good visibility and fairly near water, and within it, in a central space 200 yd across, were 12—15 roughly circular territories each 20—60 yd across. Some of these were touching, sometimes overlapping, and in each was a single adult buck who spent most of his time at the centre of it where the grass was close-cropped and the ground trampled. Nevertheless, males often displayed at each other across the boundaries of their respective territories by walking towards the boundary with head lowered and feinting with their horns. Usually they had a harem of does within their territories.

△ A handy hoof for scratching an ear. ▷ Uganda kob on the alert in Elizabeth National Park. Kob have well-developed face glands, one in front of each eye and a scent gland in the groin

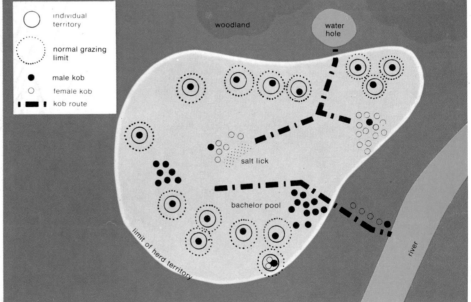

individual territory

normal grazing limit

• male kob

○ female kob

█▬█ kob route

woodland

water hole

salt lick

bachelor pool

limit of herd territory

river

Diagram of typical kob territory occupied by a medium-sized herd. Dr Hal Beuchner from his studies on kob in Toro Game Reserve in the early fifties showed how a large herd of kob scattered unevenly over the plains were actually in orderly territories (see text under Herds within herds) based upon harmless aggressive displays and fights between bucks.

Besides these circular territories, within the central space, were groups of bucks—the bachelor groups—and groups of unattached does.

The single individuals weaving restlessly through the herd are likely to be males without territories, quick and eager to get one. They wander around the edges of the central area running quickly to a particular territory and challenging the occupant, or taking possession of one temporarily vacant because its owner has led his harem to water. The males fight with feet wide apart, heads lowered and horns interlocked or beating against each other. Fights are seldom fatal; victory usually goes to the occupant male, the loser being finally chased well away towards the herd's outer boundary. Often he is chased or threatened by all the occupying males as he crosses one territory after another in his retreat.

A buck may occupy a territory for less than a day or up to 2 months.

The love kick

Breeding continues throughout the year although a female is in season for only a day. Then she leaves the unattached groups, which wander around from place to place elsewhere, and enters the territories where she mates with several males. The buck tries to attract a female with a prancing display, which often carries him in his exuberance outside his own territory, perhaps towards another male's territory, where he is chased off. Courtship includes what is known as the Laufschlag or mating kick. In this the male touches the female's underside with a stiff

The short lyre-shaped horns are a distinctive feature of the male kob (above left and centre, and previous page), the female being hornless. Kob relish tender, marshy grasses and are usually found near water. They have suffered, like many animals, from man's depletion of their habitat and unrestricted hunting.

foreleg, placing it either under her flank from the side or between her hindlegs from behind. In a great many antelopes—blackbuck, gazelle, dibatag, oryx—this is a preliminary to courtship and is a clear indication of their relationship to each other. The antelopes which do not perform the *Laufschlag* are the hartebeest—gnu—impala group, and the bovine (ox-like) group, including kudu, eland and bushbuck.

New use for old horns

Lions, leopards, hyaenas and wild dogs all prey on kob. A rather surprising predator is the python. Hay and Martin, in the *East African Wildlife Journal* for 1966 record five cases of python swallowing female kob in Uganda. It is probable, however, that even if he managed to overpower a male, a python would not be able to swallow the spreading horns.

Staking the claim

Since Buechner discovered the social behaviour of the Uganda kob, similar modes of life, with territorial and non-territorial males, have been described by Fritz Walther for Grant's and Thomson's gazelles. It was an even chance that similar territorial behaviour would be found in the puku, too. So as soon as opportunity arose, A De Vos went to the Luangwa Game Reserve to see if they, too, had such a remarkable system. He found they had but with certain differences. Puku territories were 8–20 times the size of those of the Uganda kob, and were less rigidly observed. Thus, when a male temporarily left his territory, his neighbour might wander in. The centres of the territories were not close-cropped or trampled like the kob's, perhaps because they were so much larger, with more variety of food in

them. The display which the male pukus made at each other, across their boundaries, consisted of a very rapid tail-wagging, without laying back the ears. The displays sometimes ended in a chase, which might even carry the bucks into one of the other territories. Around the territorial breeding grounds of puku are the same 'bachelor bands' as in the kob, and here too non-territorial males wander in and are chased off by the 'owner' of the territory.

class	**Mammalia**
order	**Artiodactyla**
family	**Bovidae**
genus & species	***Kobus kob*** *kob* ***K. vardoni*** *puku*

Lizard giant: a Komodo dragon takes a stroll, forked tongue flicking out to taste its way along.

Gluttons enjoy photographer's bait.

Komodo dragon

Belonging to the monitor lizards — which will be dealt with later — the Komodo dragon deserves special mention. It is not only the largest living lizard — the males grow up to 10 ft long and 300 lb weight — but also the largest lizard of all time, except for the extinct marine mosasaurs which reached 50 ft. The only known rival to the Komodo dragon is an extinct monitor in Australia of about the same size. This lived during the Miocene period, 20 — 11 million years ago. Although the Komodo dragon is so large, it was unknown outside its native home until 1912. Its native home is a few small Indonesian islands: Komodo, Rintja, Flores and Padar. The first is the largest and this is only 20 by 12 miles, the others being even smaller.

The Komodo dragon has a stout, some-what flattened body, long thick neck and longish head. Its legs are short and stout and the toes have long claws. Its tail is powerful and about the same length as the head and body combined. The tongue, which is constantly flicked out of the mouth, is long, narrow and deeply cleft. Young ones are dark in colour with red circles all over the body and vertical bands of black and yellowish green on the neck. These neck markings disappear with age but the red circles remain on the grey-brown bodies of adults.

Feats of gluttony

The islands where the Komodo dragon lives are hilly, their river beds filled only in the rainy season. The hills are covered in places with rain forest and the lowlands with tall grasses. The dragons spend the night in holes among rocks, between the buttress roots of trees or in caves. They come out at about 8.30 am to look for food — chiefly carrion, which is located by smell. The tongue seems also to be used as a taste-smell organ as in other lizards and snakes. The larger lizards monopolise any food, keeping the younger ones away by intimidating them, or beating them off with sideways sweeps of the powerful tail. Only when the bigger ones are full are the smaller able to feed. The dragons probably kill deer and pigs as well as monkeys. They eat heavy meals which last for days. An 8 ft dragon was seen to eat most of a deer, after which it rested for a week to complete the diges-tion. In eating flesh the dragon is helped by its back teeth being finely serrated, like small saws.

Young dragons feed on insects, lizards, rodents and ground-nesting birds and their eggs. Large individuals, feeding on car-cases, tear the meat apart with claws and teeth and swallow lumps whole. One was seen to gulp the complete hindquarters of a deer, another to swallow a whole monkey.

Middle-age spread

Mating takes place in July and the female lays her eggs about a month later. The eggs are oval, 4 in. long with a parchment shell, and they hatch the following April. Dragons

in zoos have grown at an average of 8 in. a year. They probably reach sexual maturity at 5 years. Up to a length of 7 ft a dragon remains slender in the body. From that size growth in length slows down markedly but there is a fairly rapid increase in girth. Earliest reports told of dragons 23 ft long and although there have been more sober reports since of 12 or 13 ft it seems that even the 10 ft usually quoted may be a few inches longer than the actual maximum measured. Reports differ so much that there can be no certainty in this respect, which is why the figure of 10 ft is to be preferred.

'Land crocodiles'

Komodo was an uninhabited island visited occasionally by pearl fishers and people hunting turtles. Then the sultan of the neighbouring island of Sumbawa used it to deport criminals and other 'undesirables'. Reports began to circulate early in the 19th century of a *boeaya-darat* or land crocodile, 23 ft long and alarmingly ferocious. In 1910 the reports became so insistent that Major PA Ouwens, director of the Botanical Gardens at Buitenzorg in Java, asked the Governor of Flores to look into the reports with the result that in 1912 Ouwens was able to publish a scientific description of this giant lizard. Then the First World War broke out and the giant was forgotten in Europe, but in 1923 Duke Adolf Friedrich von Mecklenburg, a keen explorer, went to the island of Komodo and came back with four skins of this lizard.

There are several reasons why the lizards were ignored for so long. One was that the islands were uninhabited until undesirable or doubtful characters were sent there. The stories they told were coloured by their own fears and superstitions and were so exag-gerated that they were disbelieved. The other reason was that it was called a croco-dile, and nobody in those days, before the crocodile leather craze, wanted to go all that way to look for crocodiles.

class	**Reptilia**
order	**Squamata**
suborder	**Sauria**
family	**Varanidae**
genus & species	*Varanus komodoensis*

Unique photograph of a Komodo dragon swimming off Lesser Sundra Island, Indonesia.

Kookaburra

The kookaburra or laughing jackass, although a member of the kingfisher family, appears very drab when compared with its brilliantly coloured relatives. The famous naturalist, John Gould, writing in 1844, called it the great brown kingfisher. Yet no kingfisher is better known, in its native land or throughout the world, or has been given so many different names. The one by which it is affectionately known to many Australians is 'Jackie'.

The laughing kookaburra, as it tends to be called now in Australian books, is 17 in. long, its plumage a mixture of white, buff, brown and black. It is stockily built with the usual heavy head of its family and the bill is large and heavy. The kingfisher family is divided into two subfamilies, the river kingfishers and the forest kingfishers which usually live far from water; the kookaburra is the largest of the forest kingfishers. Its range is eastern and southern Australia from Cape York in the north to Eyre Peninsula and Kangaroo Island. It was introduced into Western Australia in 1898 and is established in the southwestern corner. It was introduced into Tasmania in 1905 and is firmly settled there.

The blue-winged kookaburra is less well known. Its range is the northern parts of the continent, north of a line from Shark's Bay in Western Australia to southeastern Queensland. It is also found in New Guinea. It is the same size as the laughing kookaburra, and has much the same habits, but it is less vociferous and is mainly distinguished by the blue in its wings.

Popperfoto

HJ Pollock: Photo Res

The bushman's clock

▷ The laughing jackass or kookaburra is famous for its fiend-like screams and vulgar chuckles.
◁ Bills skywards and tails cocked a pair of 'Jackies' salute the day. To the visitor they may be attractive but Australians call them many unprintable names.
△ It is also famous as a killer of snakes, the bird above having a vice-like grip on a small but deadly poisonous one.
▽ The less well known blue-winged kookaburra. It is also known as the barking jackass as a discordant scream is added to the laughing chorus. This shy bird is usually seen in pairs or small parties and has much the same habits as the laughing jackass.

C Frith

the nest was finally 3 in. below ground level. One egg was laid then a second the next day and a third 3 days later. Male and female shared the incubating for 25 days. Several times the hen rapped on the tree with her bill. The male responded to this by going in and relieving her at the nest. This should be compared with the kiwi's behaviour. Kookaburras are vigorous in defending their nest and young.

Danger from immigrants

Away from the homesteads and suburbs the kookaburra is threatened by the continued felling of trees and from the advance of human settlement. They are also harassed by introduced starlings taking over the nesting sites in hollow trees. A further menace is that immigrants are apt to shoot the kookaburra for sport.

The vanished nest

A few years ago two men were clearing an area of bush when they noticed two kookaburras returning at intervals to fly to an 'imaginary' spot in the air about 12 ft up, hover there for a few seconds and then fly away. This was at the spot where the men had felled a tree which held a nest. The birds continued this behaviour for days.

We talk with a certain amount of wonder about swallows returning in spring, after an absence of 6 months or more, from South Africa 6 000 miles away, to the same barn or stable to nest on the same rafter. Memory and the use of landmarks are involved and presumably the landmarks are of two kinds: the gross features of the landscape and the smaller details immediately surrounding the barn window, rafters and the rest.

If resident birds such as thrushes are studied from early nesting, the gross landmarks are found to be of the most importance. For example, a thrush may start to build a nest when the trees are leafless and, sometimes within a matter of days if the weather suddenly turns mild, the whole of its surroundings have changed as the buds burst and the leaves unfold. Although the detailed picture of the surroundings is altered, the thrush continues to find its nest, suggesting the bird relies more on the gross features for its bearings.

This seems to be supported and emphasized by the behaviour of the kookaburras. Heavy tree clearance must have entirely altered the detailed picture immediately around the nest, and also the more immediate gross features, as the trees around the nest were being continually grubbed out. For the kookaburras to have been able to fly up into the space, where their nest used to be, they would seem to have been relying on the more distant features of the landscape for their bearings.

Kookaburra emerging from its nesting burrow tunnelled into a termite nest on a tree. After the bird abandons the nest at the end of the breeding season, the active termites patch up the hole.

Good or bad timekeeper?

The original habitat of the laughing kookaburra is open forested country where it can be seen in pairs, singly or in small groups. It has taken readily to parks and gardens, and becomes friendly with people, accepting food from them and tapping on windows to be fed. Because it is a nest robber its relations with small birds are not good. They harass it by flying at it, striking with wings, feet and beak.

Its outstanding feature is the sounds it makes. Gould wrote: 'It rises with the dawn when the woods re-echo with its gurgling laugh; at sunset it is again heard.' Various naturalist authors have since referred to the regularity with which the kookaburra gives out its 'shouting, whooping and laughing chorus'. It has been called the clock bird, bushman's clock and settler's clock but opinions differ on this. Some Australians say the chorus is at dawn and sunset, others that it is at dawn, noon and sunset, and there are yet others that claim the bird's laughing call can be heard at any time of the day. One who had reason to favour the third of these was thrown from his horse

and 'a pair of Jackasses in a nearby dead tree burst into a loud chorus, easily understood to be ridicule at my discomfiture'.

Snake-killer

The laughing kookaburra will eat anything animal including large insects, crabs, fish, reptiles and birds. It will not only rob nests of wild birds but has the reputation of taking chicks and ducklings from farms. It is also reputed to be a snake-killer, tackling snakes up to 2½ ft long, seizing them behind the head, battering them senseless or killing them by dropping them from a height. Several kookaburras may combine to kill a large snake.

Calling the watch

The breeding season is September—December. The nest is built in a hollow tree or in a hole in a bank, sometimes in a chamber tunnelled out of a termites' nest. The eggs are white, somewhat rounded, and there are 2—4 in a clutch. A detailed account has been given of a nesting pair in a zoo. The nest was in the hollow base of a tree and the birds tunnelled out the earth below so that

class	**Aves**	
order	**Coraciiformes**	
family	**Alcedinidae**	
genus & species	***Dacelo leachi***	blue-winged kookaburra
	D. gigas	kookaburra

Krill

Krill is a Norwegian word for the food of whalebone whales. It usually refers to the crustacean **Euphausia superba** *and this species is the one dealt with here. The word must have had a wider connotation since it was first used by Norwegian whalers in Arctic waters, and oceanographers speak of a northern krill, in the Arctic, and a southern krill, both made up of species of* **Euphausia**. *The interest today in krill is twofold. It is being suggested as a source of food for the world's expanding populations, and there is a scientific puzzle: to know how whales find krill.*

E. superba looks like a shrimp, 2 in. long with antennae adding another 1 in. It has a pair of stalked compound eyes, 8 pairs of branched legs on the abdomen, the last pair forming the tail fan. There are also 10 light organs, one at the base of each eye-stalk, 2 pairs on the underside of the thorax, at the bases of the second and seventh thoracic legs, and there is a line of 4 under the abdomen. The body of the krill is translucent but has numerous blotches and spots of reddish-brown. At night E. superba — aptly named the superb euphausian! — lights up and a shoal becomes a mass of living blue-green fire.

Restless shoals

Krill is the sole food of the large whalebone whales in the Antarctic as well as the main food of the mis-named crabeater seals, Adélie and gentoo penguins. Moreover, 32 species of fish and 7 other species of birds feed on it. It forms the most important part of the Antarctic zooplankton, being present in large shoals which, when near the surface, appear to colour the water brickred. Some shoals may be a few feet across, others may cover half an acre. In his *Great Waters* Sir Alister Hardy has described how the smaller shoals may have an indefinite outline, like that of a gorse bush, while other shoals extend in long wavy bands from one to several feet or even yards across. They may be circular, oval or oblong, often having the shape of huge amoebae. Even the smaller shoals consist of thousands of euphausians all swimming round and round in a whirling mass that continually changes shape. At one moment they are at the surface and the sea appears blood-red, at another they go deeper so their colour changes to brick-red, or they may go deeper still — to as much as 180 ft. Between the shoals are wide gaps of sea in which no krill is to be found.

Astronomical krill

A more vivid idea of the abundance of Antarctic krill can be conveyed by a few statistics. During January to April the shoals contain about 35 lb of krill per cu yd and during this time whales are estimated to eat 150 million tons. The present annual world catch of marine animals, including fish as well as whales and smaller sea foods, is said to be 60 million tons and with better methods of fishing this could be expanded to 80—90 million tons. These figures have been presented by Russian biologists who point out that, on present showing, there will be a need to increase this last figure of 80—90 to 130—150 million tons by 2000 AD if people are to be adequately fed, and they see in krill one of the few large sources of food that could be exploited. The populations of whalebone whales have been reduced in the past 40 years by 85—90%. Allowing that other species may have benefited from this, the 32 fish species, the birds and the seals, it still means a vast harvest of krill to be tapped — if only an economic method can be found. Krill contains 7% fat and 16% protein.

Complex life history

The spawning season begins in November or December and lasts 5½ months. The sperms are oval and pass from the testis into a sac. The walls of this secrete a horny cuticle to enclose them within a slender-necked, flask-shaped spermatophore. At mating this is passed out and a hand-like organ on the first of the abdominal legs, the petasma, holds the spermatophore and attaches it accurately to the opening of a pouch on the female's body just beside where the eggs will pass out, so the sperms fertilise the eggs as they are laid. It is believed the females go deep to spawn. From each egg hatches a nauplius, this changes to a metanauplius, then follow three calytopis stages and four furcilia stages. That is, the larval krill goes through 9 stages or changes at each of which it grows to look more and more like an adult. The males take 22 months to reach maturity, the females, 25 months. During the course of these changes the growing krill are moving up from depths of 750 ft, where the eggs were shed, to the surface waters.

Shrimp that feeds an ocean: **Euphausia superba**, *staple diet of many Antarctic animals.*

Chris Howell-Jones

First catch your krill

One outstanding scientific problem is whales' methods of finding krill shoals. Although we are told krill lives in huge shoals, the Antarctic Ocean represents a vast stretch and there are big gaps between the concentrations. Moreover, they do not just stay passively at the surface waiting for the whales to come along and scoop them up by the hundredweight. If krill is to be cropped successfully for the human table some way must be found of locating the shoals without too much expenditure of ship/man hours.

Krill feeds on microscopic plant plankton but the surprise is that there are no krill where the plant food is densest. This may be because, as there is reason to believe from other sources, a 'bloom' of plant plankton actually poisons animals in the sea. Two suggestions have been made to account for the 'blooms'. One is that an upwelling of water rich in phosphates causes rapid multiplication of diatoms and other plankton plants. The other is that the melting of the pack ice lets in the sun, causing the plants to increase enormously under the influence of the solar rays. Perhaps then the plant plankton has to die down or disperse before the krill can approach it safely. Whatever it is this is still an unsolved problem after years of research — and it could have an important bearing on how to harvest krill.

phylum	**Arthropoda**
class	**Crustacea**
order	**Euphausiacea**
genus & species	**Euphausia superba**

▽ *A mountain of krill from a sliced whale stomach.*

National Institute of Oceanography

Kudu

Kudu are among the largest of the antelopes. There are two species; their name is also spelt koodoo and, in South Africa, koedoe. Like their closest relatives the bushbuck and nyala they have spirally twisted horns, white spots and chevrons on the face and white stripes on the flanks. Only the males have horns, with at least 2½ turns compared with 1½ turns in related species. The greater kudu stands 50 in. or more at the shoulder, has a thick upright mane extending to the back, and a throat fringe. Its coat is reddish-fawn becoming blue-grey in old males. There are 4—10 white stripes on the flanks and the horns average 46 in. long. A male weighs up to 570 lb, a female up to 376 lb. The lesser kudu, up to 40 in. high, has a scanty mane, is yellow-grey with 11—14 white flank stripes, a white crescent on the throat, another on the chest and white spots on cheeks and nose.

The greater kudu lives in isolated hilly districts in dry country from Lake Chad, Ethiopia and Somalia, through eastern Africa to South Africa. It is more scattered than the lesser kudu, living in scrub and desert bush in eastern Ethiopia, Somalia and north and east Kenya.

A hybrid between the two was shot in the early 1960s in southern Somalia.

An antelope that somewhat resembles the kudu is the bongo, a heavily-built forest animal about 48—50 in. high, which stands somewhere between the kudu-bushbuck group and the eland. Like the eland it has a tufted tail, the females have horns and it lacks inguinal glands; like the kudu and bushbuck it has horns with a fairly open spiral, and it lacks the eland's dewlap and forehead 'mat' of hair. The horns of the bongo have only one turn and they have peculiar yellow tips. Its coat is reddish, with many stripes, chevrons and facial spots like the lesser kudu. It is confined to the forest belt of Africa, along the Guinea coast to Cameroun, across the Congo and into some isolated highland forests, 7 000—10 000 ft up, in East Africa: the Aberdares, Mt Kenya, the Mau Escarpment and the Cherangani Hills. As we shall see later, the bongo's habitat may be that of the ancestors of all this group of antelopes.

Group harmony

Kudu go about in small groups, usually of 2—4 but sometimes up to 11, and about one individual in 20 is solitary. The smaller groups may be all males or all females, with their calves, the larger groups being made up of both sexes with about two females to every male. The members of a group keep a certain distance apart while feeding, but when they lie down they come close together. They then often indulge in mutual grooming, which can be intensive, the groomers licking each other on the head

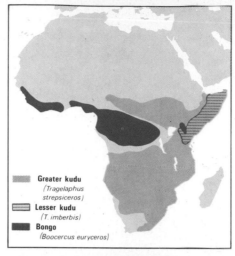

Greater kudu
(Tragelaphus strepsiceros)

Lesser kudu
(T. imberbis)

Bongo
(Boocercus euryceros)

△ *Disdain: a haughty male greater kudu.*
▽ *Shy beauty: a female greater kudu.*

▽ *Antelope banquet: a young bongo crops its way through luxuriant ground vegetation.*

and foreparts. The high-ranking animals, always males, choose which way the group shall go or when it shall lie down. Should a low-ranking animal lie down first the dominant one will make it get up again. But when it lies down, a dominant kudu seems to lose status: younger animals, and females, often come and annoy him, which they would not do if he were standing up.

Kudu are largely browsers; but they turn to eating grass, mainly during the rainy season. Their main enemies are leopards, wild dogs and lions.

Courtship wrestling

Mating takes place at all times of the year, but there is a peak in the late part of the year south of the equator, in Zambia and South Africa, and one in the early part of the year in northern Kenya, north of the equator. Gestation is 212 days. Little real fighting occurs in the rut, but males spar and threaten each other at any time. One male will try to catch another's head from the front, cross horns, and push with his forehead. During pauses in these 'wrestling matches' the opponents turn their heads away from each other, and again at the end of the fight. Probably the fights do no more than maintain or decide social dominance. Neck-fighting also is used between males, and between male and female during courtship. Males often attack trees and bushes and dig up the ground—a behaviour which has been interpreted as a re-directed threat, when an animal's aggressive courtship behaviour is frustrated.

Although females will attack males or each other, a male will not attack a female. They shove with the forehead like the males although they have no horns, ramming their opponent in the shoulder or flank, often snapping the jaws, things no male would ever do. A young bull attacked by a female may threaten her, but will not defend himself—an early example of chivalry!

In the courtship ritual the male and female wrestle with their necks. The male drives a female as a sheepdog rounds up a sheep: he overtakes her and brings her to a halt. He pushes his head and neck outstretched along her back from the rear before mounting her. He will display to the female with head upstretched, while the female lifts her nose high. If she attempts to move away, the male greater kudu may plough the ground in front of her with his horns. The male lesser kudu simply runs in front of his female to stop her.

There is one calf at a birth and this is hidden in dense cover, in a place which it selects itself by instinct. Its coat is a light cinnamon colour. The mother grooms its whole body—not just the foreparts, as when adults groom each other—and in its first few days she eats its faeces and drinks its urine, a precaution which guards against the calf's resting place being betrayed by odour. The mother lies far from her calf, though always within sight. Whenever it stands up, she goes to join it. When she moves towards it for suckling, she calls it with a soft smacking sound.

▷ *Like all antelopes, kudu are at their shyest at the waterhole. Here a group of two bulls and two cows scan the surrounding countryside.*

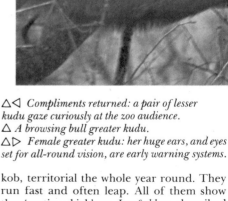

All kinds of cattle

Antelopes, sheep, goats and cattle all belong to the family Bovidae. They all have hollow horns, made up of a horny sheath on an air-filled bony core. This distinguishes them from deer, with their solid branching antlers shed every year, and from the giraffe, and the pronghorn, the so-called antelope of North America.

Evidence is accumulating to show that the various groups within the Bovidae have had a long separate history. The early research on fossils by Guy Pilgrim, and more recently by Alan Gentry, with modern work on blood groups by Vincent Sarich show that 30 million years ago the family was well estab-

lished and already splitting into the groups that exist today. The behavioural studies by Fritz Walther seem to show that the Bovidae can be divided into an ox-like group and a goat-like group, and that the term 'antelope' does not refer to a natural grouping. An antelope is, in fact, just a slenderly built ox-like member of the family Bovidae.

The gazelles, blackbuck, reedbuck, water-buck, oryxes and their relatives are 'goat-like', and are closely connected to the sheep and goats through intermediate forms like the saiga, chiru, chamois, serow and goral. Basically they are animals of the open plains; they live in large herds which break up in the mating season, the males often becom-ing territorial at that time, or are, like the

△◁ *Compliments returned: a pair of lesser kudu gaze curiously at the zoo audience.*
△ *A browsing bull greater kudu.*
△▷ *Female greater kudu: her huge ears, and eyes set for all-round vision, are early warning systems.*

kob, territorial the whole year round. They run fast and often leap. All of them show the 'mating kick' or *Laufschlag*, described under kob (p 1254). They have a pattern of longitudinal light and dark stripes, often altered into a 'harness' pattern or white eye-ring on the face, and tend to be dark above, light beneath, with a dark line running along the flanks between these. The horns tend to be rounded in section, without a keel but with prominent rings on them. The impala,

David Hughes: Photo Res

roebild

hartebeest and gnu are probably not too distantly related to the goat-like group, but form, as Alan Gentry has shown, a natural cluster a little apart.

The other group, the ox-like group, includes not only cattle, bison and buffaloes but also the nilgai and its relatives the four-horned antelope, the kudu-bushbuck-nyala group, the bongo, eland and—as very primitive living representatives—the duikers. The other 'dwarf antelopes', like the dik-diks, suni, oribi and klipspringer, belong to the goat-like group. The ox-like group are basically animals of forested country; they live singly, in pairs or in small groups; they do not run very fast but usually slip silently away into cover at sign of danger; and when

they hear a suspicious sound they suddenly freeze in mid-stride. They leap over obstacles like the bongo, or crawl under them. None shows the *Laufschlag*. The coat pattern consists of white spots on the face and jaw, white ear-rims, white marks on the limbs, and often white stripes and spots on the body; the belly is not markedly lighter than the upperside. The horns have no rings on them but are generally keeled, at least along the front surface.

The behaviour and colour-pattern of the 'ox-like group' are both adaptations to a forest environment. Some of the members, especially the eland and the Cape buffalo, have come out onto the plains and live today in herds, and the pattern is weakly expressed.

The kudu shows a transitional stage; both species live in bush country with some cover, and are decidedly not typical plains animals. The bongo lives, like its ancestors, in dense forest, and is brightly coloured with white stripes, breaking up the outline and making a good concealing coloration.

class	**Mammalia**
order	**Artiodactyla**
family	**Bovidae**
genera & species	***Tragelaphus strepsiceros*** *greater kudu*
	T. imberbis *lesser kudu*
	Boocercus euryceros *bongo*

Lacewing

The lacewing's delicate gauzy wings and rather feeble flight could well have influenced artists who were portraying fairies. Several insect families of the order Neuroptera are given this name. The most familiar in Europe are the green lacewings Chrysopidae, most of which have a green body and metallic golden eyes. All this beautiful coloration fades after the insect is dead. The brown lacewings Hemerobiidae, smaller and brown or grey, are quite common among bushes and rank herbage. The spongilla flies or sponge flies Sisyridae are small lacewings whose larvae are aquatic and live as parasites on freshwater sponges. The largest of all is the giant lacewing **Osmylus fulvicephalus**, which has a 2in. wingspan and is found near woodland streams. The tiny 'dusty-wing' lacewings Coniopterygidae are inconspicuous but of economic importance as their larvae prey on the red spider mite, a serious pest of fruit trees.

Malodorous beauty

Most lacewings fly at night and are attracted to artificial light. Green lacewings often fly out by day when bushes and low branches are disturbed, and the small brown Hemerobiidae can be found by shaking leafy branches over an inverted umbrella. Some may fly up but most will fall into the umbrella. The beautiful giant lacewing is best found by searching in culverts and bridges through which small streams run. It is a local and not very common insect. The giant and some of the green lacewings have a strong and unpleasant odour, which protects them against birds and other predators.

The larvae of the giant lacewing live in wet moss beside streams and those of the spongilla flies are wholly aquatic, breathing by means of gills. Most other lacewing larvae live among foliage.

Pincushion eggs

Lacewings undergo a complete metamorphosis, with larva, pupa and imago stages. The female green lacewing has the amazing habit of laying her eggs on the ends of long, hair-like stalks which she makes herself in groups in leaves. She first dabs a drop of gummy liquid from the tip of her abdomen onto the leaf and then, raising her abdomen, draws it up into a slender stalk which immediately hardens. The egg is then laid at the top of this stalk. The larvae are predatory, feeding largely on aphids. When fully grown each spins a cocoon of white silk given out from a spinneret which is at the hind end of the body, not on the head as in the silk-spinning caterpillars.

◁ *Sticky trap: a doomed lacewing struggles its last on the treacherous surface of the fly-catching plant* **Drosophyllum lusitanicum**. *The hundreds of glands on stalks secrete sticky fluid, while others on the surface react to the presence of the animals caught on it by giving out digestive juices. In Morocco these plants are kept indoors as living flypapers.*

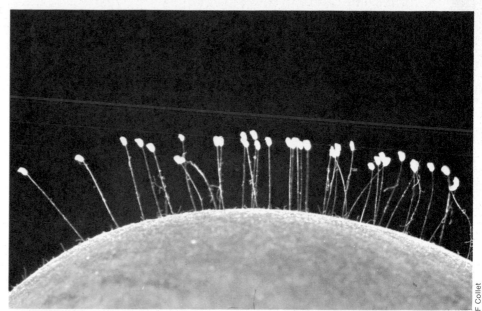

F Collet

△ *Eggs aloft: eggs of lacewing* **Chrysopa** *on the hardened gum stalks secreted by the female.*

Anthony Bannister: NHPA.

△ *Mobile litter basket: when the aphid has been sucked to a husk by this chrysopid larva its skeleton will join the remains of previous meals on its bristly back.* ▽ *Chrysopid cocoon.*

Colin Butler

The cocoons are usually attached to leaves or bark. Most of the young spend the winter as larvae inside the cocoon. They pupate the following spring, but one very common species *Chrysopa carnea* hibernates as an adult. Although it is green before hibernation, it turns brown soon after it settles down, becoming active and green again in the spring. These brown hibernating lacewings can often be seen inside houses in autumn and early winter.

The aquatic larvae of the spongilla flies *Sisyra* leave the water and spin cocoons in bark crevices and similar places. The giant lacewing spends the whole of its larval life, and spins its cocoon, in wet moss.

Hypodermic feeding

In captivity brown lacewings have been seen preying on aphids. As larvae all are predators and share with the ladybird and hoverfly larvae the task of keeping within bounds the swarming aphids or greenfly. Lacewing larvae are flattened, louse-shaped creatures with sharp-pointed, hollow jaws resembling a pair of callipers. They mostly live among foliage and crawl actively about searching for aphids and other insects. The victim is seized and pierced by the jaws through which a digestive juice is injected, liquefying the body contents. The resulting 'soup' is then sucked back by the larva. In both the injection and the suction the hollow jaws act like miniature hypodermic needles. The larvae of the larger species feed on small caterpillars and other insects as well as on aphids, and those of the giant lacewing eat any insects in their moist habitat. The smallest species prey on microscopic mites and their eggs, and in doing so may render as valuable a service as the aphid-eaters.

Anti-litter larvae

The larvae of some of the green lacewings set a wonderful example in what to do with the wrappings after an open-air meal. When one of them has sucked an aphid dry it does not throw it away but holds the husk in its jaws and presses it down onto its own back, which is covered with stiff, hooked hairs. These hold the husk in place, where it dries and shrivels. After a time the larva is covered with a mass of husks, which makes it look more like a small heap of dried rubbish than a living insect. When it moults its skin the accumulation of husks is lost, but the larva starts to replace it as soon as it begins feeding again. Most of us must have seen these disguised larvae at some time or other, on the leaves of rose bushes or other foliage, but without noticing them. Almost certainly insectivorous birds also miss them when they are searching among the leaves.

△ *Aphids beware: a chrysopid lacewing creeps down a branch in search of food.*

▽ *As remarkable for its pungent smell as its size, a giant lacewing* **Osmylus fulvicephalus**.

F Collet

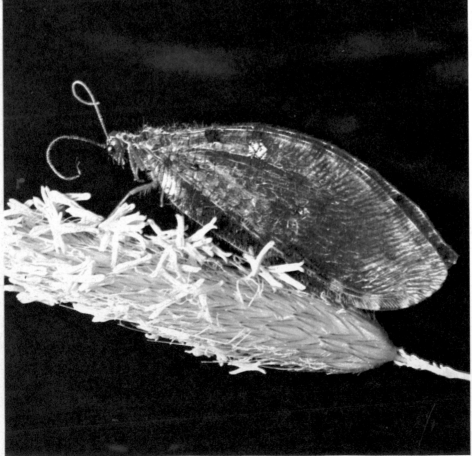

Stephen Dalton: NHPA

phylum	**Arthropoda**
class	**Insecta**
order	**Neuroptera**
families	**Chrysopidae, Hemerobiidae, Sisyridae, Osmylidae, Coniopterygidae**
genera & species	***Chrysopa carnea, Osmylus fulvicephalus, Sisyra,*** *others*

Ladybirds' winter resort
*Thousands of potato ladybirds **Epilachna dregei** hibernating together on a rockface in the Transvaal high veld.*

Ladybird

Small, brightly coloured beetles, oval or almost circular in outline, ladybirds were regarded with affection long before it was realised they are useful as well as pretty. The name ladybird (sometimes ladybug or lady beetle) dates from the Middle Ages when the beetles were associated with the Virgin Mary and called 'beetles of Our Lady'. Their coloration is generally red or yellow with black spots and the pattern tends to be variable, extremely so in some species. A few, like that known as **Coccidula rufa**, are brown without conspicuous markings, and are not usually recognised as ladybirds. The colourful species have a strong and unpleasant smell and they taste equally bad. Their bright colours doubtless serve as a warning to predators not to try to eat them. Both ladybird adults and their larvae prey on aphids,

Life in a larder

△ *The lunate ladybird of the South African high veld* **Chilomenes lunata** *laying a batch of eggs. There are 5—50 in a batch, but the beetle lays several batches, usually to a total of about 150 eggs, though 1 000 has been recorded. To provide for the young, the female lays them in an aphid-infested place. They hatch in about 3 weeks.*

◁ *Eggs of the lunate ladybird hatching. The larvae will start their aphid massacre, made easy by the mother's consideration and the soft, defenceless prey, straight away. The massacre continues even after pupation. Some idea of the extent of aphid and scale insect control by ladybirds can be had from the record of a single larva's eating 90 adult and 3 000 larval scale insects. This appetite, and the high rate of reproduction, make it a very beneficial beetle.*

▽ *Scourge of the aphids: larvae of the S. African ladybird* **Cryptolaemus** *hunting. Protected by a waxy secretion, then by warning colours, and a vile taste as adults—an easy life at all stages.*

destroying them in great numbers.

The four commonest species in Britain are the two-spot, ten-spot, seven-spot and twenty-two-spot ladybirds. The first is red with a single black spot on each wingcase but black specimens with four red spots are common, and the beetle is sometimes yellow with black spots. The underside and legs are black. The second is reddish or yellow, usually with five black spots on each wingcase, but the ground colour may be black as in the last species. The underside is brown and the legs yellowish. The seven-spot is larger than the first two species and its colours hardly vary at all. It is orange-red with a black spot on the line dividing the wingcases and three others farther back on each side. The last is much smaller with 11 black spots on each side on a bright yellow ground. The largest and most handsome British species is the eyed ladybird **Anatis ocellata**, which has black spots on a red ground, each spot being

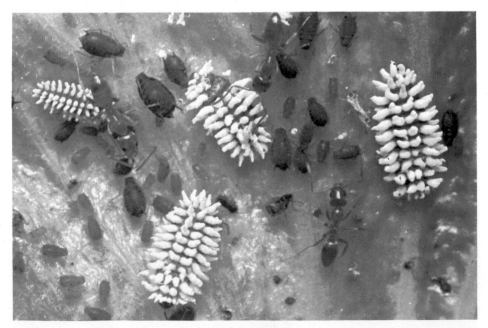

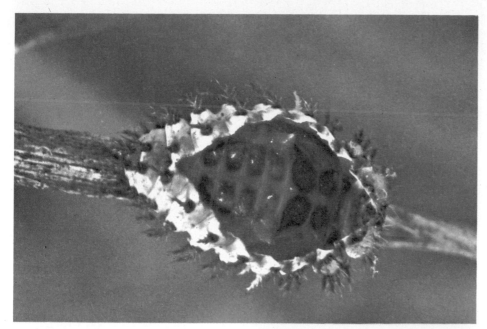

△ *A pupa, the ladybird's only lull in feeding.*

▷ *Full circle: adult lunate ladybirds
feeding on a liberal supply of aphids.*
Even man, for hundreds of years, has contributed
to the ladybirds' mollycoddled existence by
recognising the need to keep them alive. They
have even taken their place in English folklore
with the rhyme 'Ladybird, ladybird, fly away
home, your house is on fire, your children alone',
a reference to the custom of burning hop vines
at the end of the season, no doubt with many
larvae on them. The second stanza, 'Except little
Nan, who sits in a pan, weaving gold laces as
fast as she can' concerns the colourful larva
weaving a pupal case. These lines, spoken when
a ladybird landed nearby, must have saved many
an extremely useful insect's life by staying the
hand that instinctively swats everything that
crawls.

▽ *The black sheep: one of the few vegetarian
ladybirds **Epilachna dregei** which spoil
the group's fine reputation by feeding on
potato leaves.*

surrounded by a halo of yellow. It may be
$\frac{2}{8}$ in. long and lives among pine foliage.

The first four of these have been given
the scientific names **Adalia bipunctata,
A. decempunctata, Coccinella
septempunctata** and **Thea vigintiduo-
punctata** respectively. Even scientists
sometimes jib at long names so these four
ladybirds are usually referred to as
2-punctata, 10-punctata, 7-punctata
and **22-punctata**.

Crowded winter resorts

In summer ladybirds fly actively about
among foliage. In winter they hibernate as
adults, often in large groups. Sometimes 50
or 100 of them can be found crowded together under a piece of loose bark, on a
post or in a porch. They often congregate
in houses and usually go unnoticed until
they come out in spring. In California crevices and caves on certain hilltops are well
known as hibernation resorts where ladybirds gather in their thousands.

Hordes and hordes of ladybirds

Ladybirds usually lay their orange-coloured
eggs on the undersides of leaves, in batches
of 3—50. Several batches are laid by one
female, totalling 100—200 eggs, sometimes
more. Because the beetles themselves feed
on aphids or greenfly they tend to choose
places where these are abundant in which
to lay, so the larvae find food handy from
the start. The eggs hatch in from 5 to 8 days,
turning grey shortly before they do so. The
larvae are active, bristly and variously
coloured in patterns of black, orange, blue
and red. Like the adult beetles they feed on
aphids, but since they are growing rapidly
they are far more voracious. The larval
stage lasts 3 weeks or so, during which time
several hundreds of aphids are eaten.

When thousands of aphid-eating ladybirds are each laying hundreds of eggs and
every larva is consuming hundreds of
aphids, it can be imagined that very large
numbers of greenfly are destroyed, and the
benefit to plants, both wild and cultivated, is
enormous. The pupa is usually attached to

Photographs by Anthony Bannister: NHPA

a leaf. The whole life cycle takes from 4 to 7 weeks, so several generations of ladybirds may be produced in a summer.

One small group of ladybirds are not predatory but feed as larvae on plant food. A single species occurs in Britain, the twenty-four-spot ladybird *Subcoccinella viginti-quatuorpunctata* (certainly better written *24-punctata*), which eats clover.

Ladybird farms

The principle of using one species of insect to control the numbers of another is now well known, and is often advocated as being preferable to the use of poisonous insecticides. An early example of an operation of this kind concerns the use of a ladybird. Towards the end of the last century the Californian citrus orchards were devastated by the cottony-cushion scale insect, which was accidentally introduced from Australia. A brightly coloured ladybird *Rhodalia cardinalis* was found to be a natural enemy of the scale insect in Australia, and in 1889 some of these ladybirds were brought to California and released in the orchards. They effectively controlled the scale insect there and they have since been introduced to South Africa.

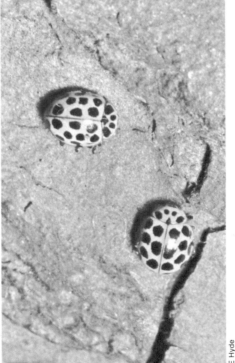

The Californian citrus growers were also troubled by aphids and other plant bugs, and use was made of a native ladybird, a species of *Hippodamia,* that hibernates, as mentioned earlier, in caves in the hills. These were collected and sold to the citrus farmers by the litre (8 000 to 10 000 beetles in each litre) and later by the gallon. This control was started in 1910, neglected, then revived during the Second World War.

Even this is not the end of the story of useful ladybirds in California. In the 1920s the orchards were attacked by another scale insect *Pseudococcus*. Again a ladybird was brought from Australia, by the name of *Cryptolaemus montrouzieri*. This failed to breed under natural conditions in Western America, so huge ladybird factories were maintained where they were bred, with careful control of temperature and other conditions, on potato shoots infested with *Pseudococcus*. In 1928 alone 48 million ladybirds of this species were set free in the Californian orange orchards.

class	**Insecta**
order	**Coleoptera**
family	**Coccinellidae**

△ *One of the commonest English ladybirds, the two spot* **Adalia bipunctata.**
▷ *The writing on the wings: the unusual markings of* **Coccinella hieroglyphica.**

△ *The lighter colour variation of* **Calvia 14-guttata.**
▷ *A unique photograph of* **Coccinella septempunctata** *taking off.*

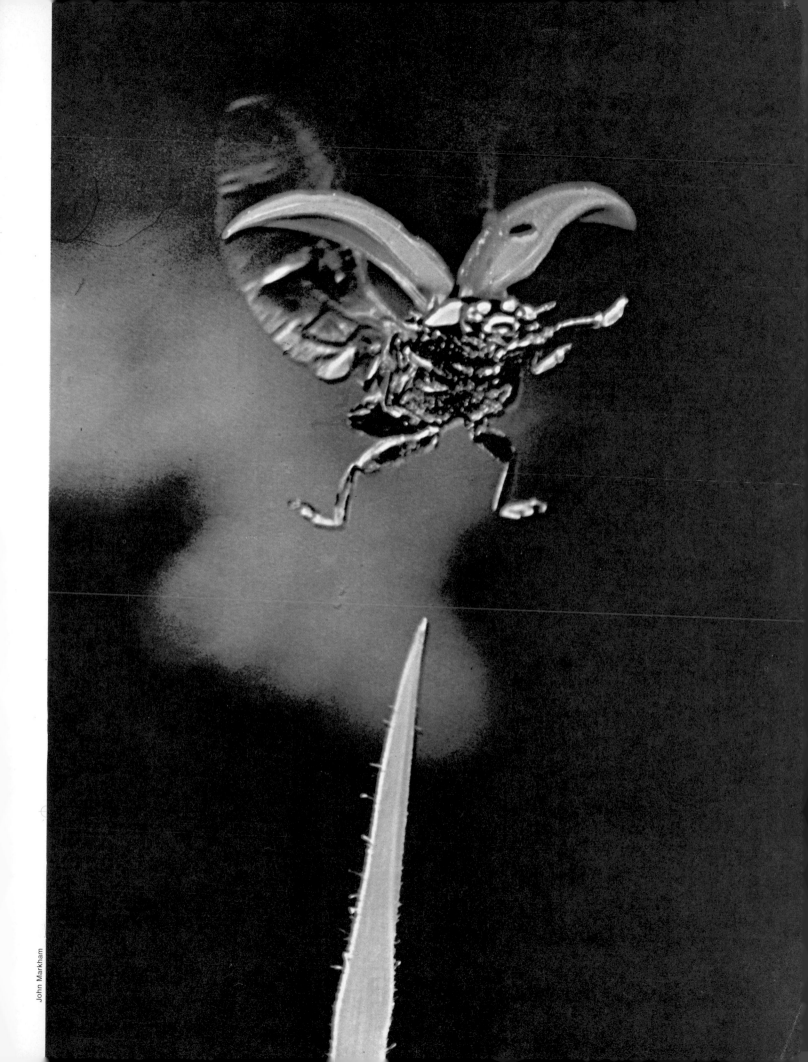

Lammergeier

A huge, graceful, and much-maligned vulture, the lammergeier has a wingspan of 8½–9 ft. The plumage is very distinctive: the head is white with a black mask running from the eyes to tufts of feathers on each side of the bill, giving the lammergeier its alternative name of bearded vulture. In flight, the lammergeier is readily identified by the long wings and long diamond-shaped tail. The underparts are a light rusty colour and the wings, tail and back are greyish-black. Young lammergeiers, up to the age of 5 years, are dark brown.

The lammergeier ranges from southern Europe, including Spain, Sardinia, Corsica, Sicily, Switzerland, Greece and the Balkans, through the Middle East to northern India, Tibet and southern China. It is also found in parts of north-west, northeast, eastern and southern Africa. It lives in mountainous districts such as the sierras of Spain and the Himalayas, coming out onto the plains only to forage. In some parts such as Tibet it is common and is often found near human settlements where it will run about near man, but in other parts it is rare. In Basutoland, for example, there are only 20 pairs left.

Mountain vulture

Lammergeiers combine an almost regal appearance and an extreme grace in flight with a cowardice out of all proportion to their size. In flight they are magnificent, being numbered among the most skilled gliders. They soar over mountain passes or glide close to the ground following the contours, hardly ever beating their wings. In a gentle glide they have been timed to fly at 80 mph. Like all vultures, they are carrion eaters. They circle an animal, or land and watch it from a safe distance until they are sure it is dead. Other vultures such as the griffon vulture or white-backed vulture keep lammergeiers from a carcase until they have finished, so the lammergeiers have to make do with the bones and scraps.

Scavengers of carrion

Lammergeiers are scavengers eating mainly carrion, although they sometimes take live prey. Around human habitations they eat any carrion or offal, including human corpses, and search rubbish dumps for edible scraps and manure heaps for maggots. They seem to be particularly fond of bone marrow, swallowing small bones whole or dropping large bones from a height to split them. The tongue is stiff and has curved sides, apparently being used as a scoop for extracting marrow.

Inevitably, there are stories of children or lambs being seized by lammergeiers, but evidence—for the former at least—is never more than circumstantial. It has been pointed out that even if this cowardly bird attacked a child it would be unable to carry it away because its talons, which look so formidable, are very weak. Lammergeiers have,

Kaj Boldt

△ *Distinguished beard and feathered neck make the lammergeier a dandy among vultures.*

▽ *A lammergeier considers discretion the better part of valour and waits for its cousins to finish*

their meal before sharing the scraps with a white-necked raven **Corvultur albicollis.**

△ *The lucky one: food requirements force the mother to kill all but one of her chicks.*

MP Price

however, been described as swooping at goats or chamois and knocking them over cliffs, and mountaineers have also reported being attacked in this manner.

Nesting on mountains

Each pair of lammergeiers owns a large territory which they rarely leave. Within the territory they build a nest of sticks, wool and other material including bones and horns. The nest is often of considerable size, 8 ft across and 2 ft deep, built on inaccessible crags, on ledges, in caves or niches. During the breeding season the lammergeiers, like eagles and other hawks, perform spectacular displays. They swoop and soar together, sometimes diving several hundred feet and occasionally they roll onto their backs and grapple with their talons.

One or two, rarely three, eggs are laid. They are pale pink with brown and purple mottling. The female incubates most of the time, especially at night, and the eggs hatch after 53 days. It appears that one chick is killed shortly after hatching and only one is reared. This may be a device to limit the offspring to the number that the parents can adequately feed. If they tried to rear both, one would probably die of starvation.

The white-coated chick is brooded by both parents for 3 weeks. After that it is often left by itself while its parents are away foraging. They bring food back in the talons or bill, or they may regurgitate it into the nest from the crop. The chick has a very wide gape and can swallow large lumps of food. It can fly in about 110 days but remains in the vicinity of the nest for some time.

Bone-splitters

The habit of dropping bones to split them is unique, but it is not a habit of all lammergeiers. Nevertheless, in ancient times they were called *ossifragus* and in Spain they are still called *quebranta-huesos*, both words meaning 'bonebreaker'. The lammergeier swoops downwind, dropping the bone from a height of 100–200 ft, then immediately turns upwind and settles by the bone. This manoeuvre, turning upwind to allow it to control its flight carefully, enables the lammergeier to prevent other scavengers from stealing its booty. If the bone does not break, the manoeuvre is repeated several times. Although the lammergeier sometimes drops a bone on soft ground where it will not split, as gulls sometimes persist in dropping shellfish on soft sand, areas of rock often become strewn with fragments of bone where a lammergeier has habitually come to drop its bones.

Tortoises are treated in the same fashion and Pliny recounts how a Greek poet was killed when an 'eagle', perhaps a lammergeier, dropped a tortoise on his head. The poet had stayed out of doors all day because an oracle had foretold his death from the fall of a house!

class	**Aves**
order	**Falconiformes**
family	**Accipitridae**
genus & species	***Gypaetus barbatus***

KB Newman

Lamprey

*Lampreys look like eels and have some-times been called lamprey eels or lamper eels. They are, however, jawless like the hagfish (p 1002) their nearest relative, and, like the hagfishes, lampreys are not true fishes but direct descendants of the jawless Ostracoderms. There are about 30 species, both marine and freshwater. Some are parasitic on fish, others are not. Lampreys live in temperate regions of northern and southern hemispheres. The sea lamprey, the best known, lives on both sides of the North Atlantic. Members of the genus **Lampetra** are found in Europe and Asia as well as North America. In the southern hemisphere, species of **Geotria** and **Mordacia** are found off the coasts of Chile, Australia and New Zealand. Geotria has a large fleshy bag, of un-known function, almost hiding its mouth.*

Pump-like gills

The eel-like body of a lamprey has a slimy scaleless skin. Its fins are found along the centre-line of the body. There is a single nostril in the middle of the head, which leads behind into a blind sac. The eyes are well-developed. The head ends in front in a large funnel-like mouth with horny teeth lining the funnel, some of the teeth being on the muscular tongue protruding at the base of the funnel. Behind the head is a row of small circular gill openings running down each side of the body. Inside are seven pairs of gill pouches lined with blood-red gill-filaments which open into a tube that is blind at one end and opens into the back of the mouth in front. A lam-prey can breathe by taking in water through its mouth to pass across the gills. More often, because the mouth is so much used as a sucker, a lamprey breathes by con-tracting muscles around the gill-pouches, driving the water out. As the muscles relax water is drawn in. This pumping action seems to be helped by movements of the sinuous latticework of cartilage, the bran-chial basket, surrounding the gill-pouches.

The lamprey feeds by pressing the cir-cular edge of its mouth against the side of a fish which it finds by eyesight, not by smell as in the hagfish. It protrudes its tongue and punctures the fish's skin by rasping the teeth on it; the fish starts to bleed and the blood is sucked in by the lamprey. It sucks in a few fragments of flesh as well, but it feeds more on the blood than on the flesh. Not all adult lampreys feed in this way; some species do not feed as adults.

Lampreys barricade their nests

There are three species of lamprey in Europe. They are usually spoken of as the sea lamprey, river lamprey and brook lamprey. It is better to use the second's alternative name of lampern, because it also spends its adult life in the sea. The brook lamprey is also known as the pride. It lives all the time in freshwater. Those lampreys living in the sea enter rivers to spawn. The migration begins in winter and

Heather Angel

△ *The hooded larva of a brook lamprey.*
▽ *Lamprey skeleton showing branchial basket, which supports the gill pouches, and the viciously toothed, circular mouth cartilage, which serves instead of jaws.*
▽▽ *Powerful sucker of a brook lamprey.*

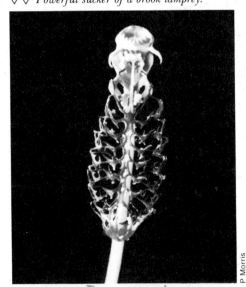

P Morris

Fritz Siedel

by spring the lampreys are in the rivers and building nests. They swim strongly and can make their way over rocks or up vertical walls, hauling themselves up with the sucker mouth. The male lamprey makes a nest by holding pebbles in its sucker mouth and moving them downstream to form a barricade. In a depression made upstream of this, the eggs will later be laid.

The females arrive later than the males and then help build the nest, the two some-times combining to move large pebbles. After spawning the adults drift downriver to die. The eggs are $\frac{1}{25}$ in. diameter and they hatch 2 weeks later. The larva, or ammo-coete, was once thought to be a different species. It is small and worm-like, and lives by burrowing in the sand or mud and com-ing out at night to feed on particles of plant and animal bodies. These are strained through fleshy tentacles (cirri) on a hood-like mouth and passed into the gullet where they are caught by sticky secretions on a special groove, the endostyle. This endo-style becomes the thyroid gland—the chemical controller of growth—in the adult.

After 3–5 years of larval life the ammo-coete, now 4–5 in. long, changes into an adult lamprey. The hooded mouth becomes funnel-shaped, the cirri are replaced by horny teeth, the nostril moves from the front of the snout to the top of the head, the eye grows larger. The sea lamprey be-comes silvery and goes down to the sea, as does the lampern, but the latter does not parasitize fishes. Instead it feeds on molluscs, crustaceans and worms. The pride or brook lamprey, which remains in rivers, does not feed when adult.

The celebrated surfeit

It is often said that King John died of a sur-feit of lampreys. It was, in fact, Henry I. It was King John who fined the men of Gloucester 40 marks because 'they did not pay him sufficient respect in the matter of lampreys'. American history is more recent and has to do with a surfeit of lampreys in the Great Lakes. Gradually, over the years, the lampreys made their way up the New York State Barge Canal and the Welland Canal and became firmly estab-lished in the Great Lakes. There they ruined a commercial fishery that had been yielding a yearly catch of 11 million pounds of lake trout and other fishes. A big research pro-gramme was set going to find ways of kill-ing off the lampreys. Weirs were built to stop further migrations into the lakes, the lampreys were poisoned and electrocuted. Some success was achieved but now that a poison that kills the larvae has been dis-covered lampreys are being wiped out and the fisheries are recovering.

class	**Marsipobranchii**
order	**Hyperoartii**
family	**Petromyzontidae**
genera & species	***Petromyzon marinus*** *sea lamprey* **Lampetra fluviatilis** *lampern* **L. planeri** *pride* *others*